Gems
&
Crystals

Gems & Crystals

AN ILLUSTRATED GUIDE TO THE HISTORY, LORE AND PROPERTIES OF GEMS & MINERALS

ANNA S. SOFIANIDES

Associate, Department of Mineral Sciences
American Museum of Natural History

and

GEORGE E. HARLOW

Curator of Gems and Minerals
Department of Mineral Sciences
American Museum of Natural History

Photographs by Erica and Harold Van Pelt

PARKGATE
BOOKS

First published in the US by Simon and Schuster, 1990
This edition published in Great Britain in 1997 by

Parkgate Books Ltd
London House
Great Eastern Wharf
Parkgate Road
London SW11 4NQ
Great Britain

1 3 5 7 9 8 6 4 2

Copyright © Nevraumont Publishing Co., Inc., 1990
Photographs Copyright © Erica and Harold Van Pelt, 1990
This edition licensed by Parkgate Books Ltd, 1997

ISBN 1 85585 391 4

Book design by Mary Moriaty

Printed and bound in Hong Kong

All photographs Erica and Harold Van Pelt except:

Department of Library Services, American Museum of Natural History,
page 9, 12-16 (left), 37, 54, 61 (left), 66, 82, 85, 91, 94, 97, 99, 111, 114,
129 (top), 133, 136, 138, 139, 147, 154, 192 (top), 197, 198

David Grimaldi, page 182

Tiffany & Co., pages 43, 173

Smithsonian Institute, page 15 (right)

Gemological Institute of America, pages 25, 27, 31, 32, 33

Acknowledgments

THERE ARE MANY PEOPLE TO WHOM THE AUTHORS ARE GREATLY INDEBTED FOR THEIR EFFORTS, ASSISTANCE, AND ADVICE.
We doubt you would be reading this book at all without the dedication, ministrations, and
good humor of Nancy Creshkoff, our stylist and editor.
The moral support, valuable advice, and infinite patience of Tom Sofianides and
Carole Slade, our spouses, were imperative to our completing this book.
Without the participation of Joseph J. Peters, including his painstaking review
of information on the collections and assistance with many aspects of this project,
it would not have come to fruition.
Peter N. Nevraumont, the producer of the book, has been very constructive with his queries,
criticisms, and suggestions.
We appreciate the patience and assistance of others in the Museum's Department of Mineral Sciences,
particularly Janice Yaklin and Charles Pearson, and at *Natural History*, L. Thomas Kelly
and Scarlett Lovell.
The Museum's photographic studio was generous with its assistance, and we thank
Jackie Beckett, Kerry Perkins, and Denis Finnin.
Many people have been generous with information: Joan Aruz, Wendy Ernst, Linda Eustis,
Leonard Gorelick, Eugene Libre, George Morgan, James Pomarico, Frank Rieger,
Peter Schneirla, David Seaman, James Shigley, and Nicholas Steiner.

WE ARE GRATEFUL TO THOSE WHO HAVE HELPED CREATE THE MINERAL AND GEM COLLECTIONS.
Those whose donations are featured in this book are as follows:
George Ackerman; Mrs. R.T. Armstrong; Mrs. Frank L. Babbott; Lilias A. Betts;
Mrs. C.L. Bernheimer; Susan D. Bliss; Maurice Blumenthal; David A. Byers;
Elizabeth Varian Cockcroft; Lawrence H. Conklin; Joseph F. Decosimo; Dr. B. Delavan;
Mrs. George Bowen DeLong; Lincoln Elsworth; Alexander J. and Edith Fuller;
Leila B. Grauert; Jack Greenberg; Peter Greenfield; K.B. Hamlin; Dr. George E. Harlow;
Mrs. William H. Haupt; Lloyd Herman; Dr. Maurice B. Hexter;
Mrs. Charles C. Kalbfleisch; Morton Kleinman; Dr. George F. Kunz; Korite Minerals, Ltd.;
Vincent Kosuga; Mabel Lamb; Charles Lanier; Gerald Leach; S. Howard Leblang;
Mrs. Zoe B. Larimer; Mrs. Bonnie LeClear estate; Vera Lounsbery estate;
Roy Mallady; Alastair Bradley Martin; Mrs. Patrick McGinnis; Roswell Miller, Jr.;
Milton E. Mohr; Dr. Arthur Montgomery; M.L. Morgenthau; John Pierpont Morgan,Sr.;
John Pierpont Morgan, Jr.; Dr. Walter Mosmann; Dr. Henry Fairfield Osborn;
Clara Peck estate; Phelps-Dodge Corporation; Dwight E. Potter; Arthur Rasch;
Dr. Julian Reasonberg; Robinson & Sverdlik Company; Mr. and Mrs. J. Robert Rubin;
Hyman Saul; Mr. and Mrs. Bernard Schiro; Elizabeth Cockcroft Schettler;
Dr. Louis Schwartz; Victoria Stone estate; William Boyce Thompson estate;
John Van Itallie; David Warburton; Thomas Whiteley; and several anonymous donors.

About This Book

Our fascination with gems and crystals spans several millennia. Gems were treasured by most of the potentates who ruled the great civilizations of the ancient world. Carnelian and rock crystal beads were fashioned in Mesopotamia during the seventh millennium B.C., and turquoise beads found there date from around 5000 B.C. Since the first colorful stones were used as objects of adornment, gemstones have been credited with magical and medicinal virtues and coveted as symbols of wealth and power. They have also been polished, shaped, engraved, and faceted to enhance their beauty; analyzed to reveal the secrets of their eye-catching colors and radiance; and exploited for their aesthetic, financial, and industrial value.

This book provides a concise but comprehensive examination of gems and gem materials, including discussion of their properties, sources, lore, and legends, as well as the history of their use and popularity in different cultures. The text encompasses a panorama of topics, ranging from the ancient lapidaries describing gems and their virtues to recent scientific discoveries and research. After providing an overview of the history of gems, the authors explore and explain the optical and crystalline properties that give gems their brilliant or colorful appearance. Separate sections are then devoted to the various gems and crystals, including organic gems (such as pearls, coral, amber, and jet) and rare and unusual stones and ornamental materials, some of them little known despite their remarkable colors and crystalline forms.

All the gems, crystals, and minerals pictured in this book come from the collections and exhibitions of the American Museum of Natural History. Surprisingly, this is the first visual record of the Museum's gem and crystal treasures to have appeared for more than fifty years – and also the first time that these spectacular treasures have been photographed comprehensively in color.

Introduction

"These gems are nice, but you know they are all fakes. The real ones are kept locked up in a vault somewhere." So I recall a visitor's remark during one of my walks through the Morgan Memorial Hall of Gems at the American Museum of Natural History. This comment is not the most disarming I have heard in that great treasure chest, but it shows some of the misconceptions that exist. If this assertion were true, the Museum's insurance agents could breathe a sigh of relief, but fortunately for the public, it is not. Everything on display is real.

More interesting to me is the level of people's appreciation. "Oh, that's the Star of India. Isn't it pretty?" This response is common but a far cry from the expert's "LOOK at that pad" (pronounced pod), in reference to our 100-carat orangy sapphire known as the variety padparadscha, "It's FANTASTIC!" Most visitors are impressed by this gem but do not know just how special it is. One of our goals here is to give you a good look at the Museum's gems and gem crystals. The more general intent is to provide information on these that is both interesting and useful.

Minerals and gems have been part of the Museum since it opened in 1869 in the old Arsenal Building in Central Park. There was a small mineral "cabinet" to instruct the public, but it was nothing to brag about. For their growth into international prominence, the collections awaited benefactors such as Charles L. Tiffany, Morris K. Jesup, and John Pierpont (J.P.) Morgan. George Frederick Kunz was a central figure; he was Tiffany & Co.'s gem expert from 1877 until he died in 1932 and during that time had a profound effect on the gem industry and the Museum's gem and mineral collections.

In 1889, a great Exposition Universelle was scheduled in Paris; it provided an opportunity for Tiffany & Co. to demonstrate to Europeans both American artistry in the form of jewelry and silver and North America's natural wealth through a collection of "Gems and Precious Stones" assembled by Kunz. He searched the continent and gathered a formidable array of stones, crystals,

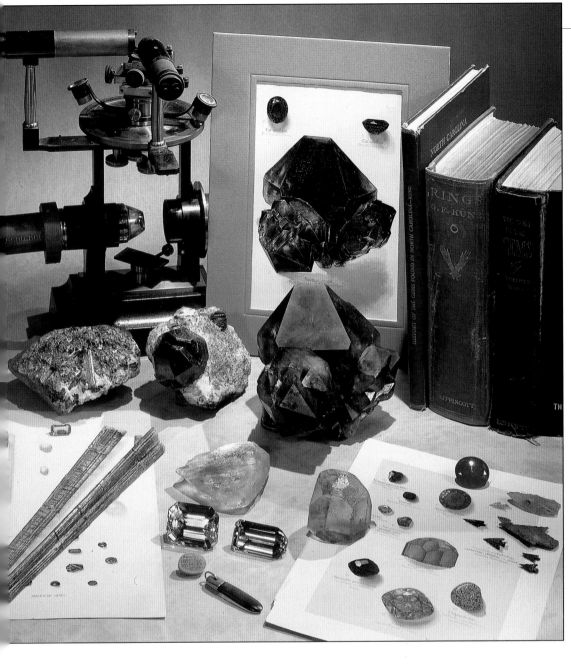

pearls, and other specimens that surprised the European audience and won the collection a gold medal. Whereas much of the Tiffany jewelry was sold then and there, the "collection" was not commercial and was brought back to New York. This was Kunz's liking, as he felt it should be kept intact, preferably coming to the American Museum of Natural History. The Museum's president, Morris K. Jesup, understood the value of the collection, but there was a problem of money—exactly $20,000. This was such a significant sum that the Museum's Board of Trustees felt inclined to question it or, at the very least, to haggle. After months of negotiations, the problem was ultimately resolved by J.P. Morgan, the banker, financier, and Museum Board member, who permitted $15,000 toward the purchase price to be "charged to his account," presumably at Tiffany & Co., which donated the remaining $5,000. Thus the Museum gained a significant gem collection in 1890, called the Tiffany Collection or Tiffany-Morgan Collection of Gems.

The same personalities and forces came together in 1900 for another Exposition Universelle in Paris. Morgan responded to the challenge and is thought to have supplied $1 million (Remember, this is 1900!) for George F. Kunz to search the world over for fabulous gems and specimens. The result was an even mightier exhibit, one that captured a grand prize. This collection, the Second Tiffany-Morgan (or Morgan-Tiffany) Collection of Gems, came directly to the Museum. The combined collections contained 2,176 specimens and 2,442 pearls and clearly laid claim to being the finest in North America, if not the world.

Morgan's interest in the gem and mineral collections continued. In 1901, he purchased for $100,000 one of the great private mineral collections created during the nineteenth century, that of Clarence S. Bement, a Philadelphia industrialist. This collection was not only superb in quality but so large that two railroad boxcars were required to bring the approximately 13,000 specimens to the Museum. This addition became the backbone of our mineral collection; many of its fine pieces are currently featured in the mineral and gem halls. Morgan's donations continued until his death in 1913.

A list of noteworthy donors to the collection would be extremely long, but I would like to mention a few more. J.P. Morgan Jr. continued his father's tradition and is responsible for many of the large fine gems, particularly a group of sapphires donated in 1927. George F. Baker, a friend of the elder J.P., funded the creation of the Morgan Memorial Hall, which opened on the Museum's fourth floor on May 1, 1922. Kunz, who was not only responsible for Morgan's gifts but for those of many others, contributed numerous specimens and several collections. He was named honorary curator of precious stones in 1904—a title never bestowed before or since. William Boyce Thompson, the founder of Newmount Mining Corporation, provided a significant fund in 1940, the earnings from which permit us to purchase specimens, for example, the Harlequin Prince black opal, a fabulous 59-carat heart-shaped morganite, and the 596-pound topaz crystal. In 1951, upon the death of Gertrude Hickman Thompson, his widow, many more magnificent gems, carvings, and minerals came to the Museum.

Some have given individual stones a spectacular that each carries the donor's name: Edith Haggin DeLong (the DeLong Star Ruby), Elizabeth Crockroft Schettler (the Schettler Emerald), and Zoe B. Armstrong (the Armstrong Diamond). Harry F. Guggenheim gave both gifts and his name to the present Hall of Minerals, which—together with the Morgan Hall of Gems—opened in May of 1976.

The most notorious event in the Department's history happened on October 29, 1964, when Jack (Murph the Surf) Murphy and two accomplices made a daring robbery of the old Morgan Memorial Hall, getting away with the Star of India, the DeLong Star Ruby, the Midnight Star, the Schettler Emerald, many other stones, and virtually all of the diamonds. Having seen the movie *Topkapi*, which depicts a fantastic burglary in the Topkapi Palace Museum in Istanbul, Murphy decided that the Morgan Hall could be entered in much the same way. He and an accomplice hid on the top floor of the Museum while another circled outside in a getaway car. The two lowered themselves by rope through an open window into the old Morgan Hall, where they literally raked the stones out of the cases with a glass cleaner. The only alarm—that for the Star of India—had a dead battery. The burglars escaped easily but were so boastful about their triumph that they were quickly apprehended, and most of the stones were returned. The DeLong Star Ruby had already gone to the underworld and had to be ransomed. Thirty-five objects have never been recovered, including the uncut 15-carat Eagle Diamond from a glacial moraine near Eagle, Wisconsin, at that time the largest diamond ever found in the United States. This unique diamond crystal and others were probably cut into gems and so permanently lost—a real tragedy.

View of the Museum from West 77th Street, from an old restored watercolor architectural rendering.

T he minerals and gems on display number approximately 5,000, roughly 2,000 in the Morgan Hall of Gems and 3,000 in the Guggenheim Hall of Minerals. The collections actually total in excess of 90,000 minerals and 3,700 gems; that is, the majority of gems are on exhibit, but only three percent of the minerals. The reason for the vastly different percentages is the nature of the materials and the multiple goals of the Museum. The gems are by definition ornamental material, demanding to be exhibited. Mineral specimens, while sometimes manifesting spectacular crystallinity, color, or form, are frequently rather visually uninteresting—what I sometimes call "uglies." We have many of these on display to show a representative spectrum of the 3,200 mineral species, but the vast majority stay behind the scenes. The value in these "hidden" specimens is their record of Earth chemistry, of mineral-forming processes, and of the ways in which atoms can be arranged. The collections are a resource to scientists from universities and museums all over the world. The beautiful counterparts to uglies, the gems and gem crystals, can be even more valuable to science because of their unusual size and the perfection of crystallinity. My own scientific research in recent years has included studies of the jadeite variety of jade, an interest first stimulated by the beautiful jade objects. However, we try to preserve the gems and beautiful crystals for both the enjoyment and edification of Museum visitors.

Collections must continue to grow to stay alive. Much as the public relies on museums to display wealth once available to only a few, museums rely on the public to share such wealth. The American tradition of generosity provides the basis of most museum collections; certainly this is true for the American Museum of Natural History. The amount of donating fluctuates with the economy (and the tax code), but we should all hope that museum collections can grow and allow all of us to see the world's treasures.

The task of presenting a superb gem and gemstone collection is a formidable one and a rare opportunity. The superb color photographs by the esteemed photographers Harold and Erica Van Pelt speak for themselves and provide a far more vibrant portrayal of the collection than the previous one, made nearly a half-century ago in drawings and black-and-white photographs by the then curator, Herbert C. Whitlock. But the collection is much more than the sum of its images; it is a diverse resource for research and education and an archive of natural perfection. In my thirteen years as curator and in my coauthor's seventeen years of working as a gemologist with the collection, we have developed a great appreciation for the gems. The text conveys some or our knowledge of them. I have focused on the distinctive properties of the gemstones and their origins, and Anna Sofianides has contributed her wealth of information on their history and lore and on gem evaluation.

This book can serve as a concise visual guide to the gem collection at the American Museum of Natural History and a compendium of gem mineral information. However, no book or photograph can rival the real thing. Gems are visual delights, and seeing them first hand is the only way to observe their character. A sparkling faceted gem comes alive with motion—the motions of the viewer, the illumination, and the stone. The same is true for asteriated gems, cat's eyes, and opals. It is no wonder that gems have long been used for human adornment, as motion is an essence of our being. Thus I encourage you, once fortified with the images and information in our book, to visit our collection in New York City and see, while you move around the exhibit, the wonderful qualities of the gems and crystals.

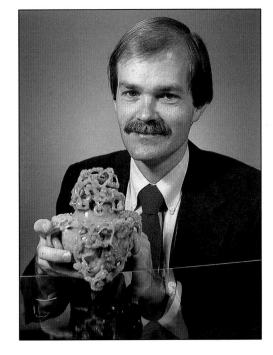

George E. Harlow
February 28, 1990

HIGHLIGHTS FROM THE MUSEUM'S

VISITORS TO MUSEUMS often ask "What are the highlights?" Gems have a very personal appeal,
in this book, are without doubt among the highlights

Manchu headdress pendant, with Imperial jadeite, pearls, sapphires, and pink tourmalines, PAGE 19.

The Lounsbery Diamond necklace, containing over 100 diamonds, PAGE 40.

The 563.35-ct. Star of India, the largest gem-quality blue star sapphire in the world, PAGE 45.

The 116.75-ct. Midnight Star, a sapphire notable for its deep purple violet color, PAGE 46.

Superb 100-ct. padparadscha sapphire, thought to be the largest on public display, PAGE 48.

The 100.3-ct. DeLong Star Ruby, which was successfully ransomed following "The Great Jewel Robbery" in 1964, PAGE 52.

The Patricia Emerald, a large twelve-side crystal famous for its perfection and superb color, PAGE 56.

Chinese carving of a sitting goddess, the finest and largest morganite carving known, PAGE 59.

Fragment from the largest aquamarine crystal ever found, which yielded around 200,000 cts. of cut gems, PAGE 62.

Official trappings of a Moroccan vizier (c. 1750), featuring aquamarines and other gems, PAGE 64.

The 87.62-ct. Schettler Emerald, engraved with a flower-and-leaf pattern, PAGE 67.

A superb 58.79-ct. morganite from the Malagasy Republic, PAGE 69.

An 85.0-ct cat's eye, PAGE 71.

Alexandrite, showing change of color in incandescent light and daylight, PAGE 74.

A 70.99-ct. spinel from Sri Lanka, PAGE 76.

The world's largest topaz crystal, weighing 271 kg (596 lb.), PAGE 82.

The largest faceted red topaz in the world, a 70.40-ct. oval brilliant-cut gem with an unusual deep red color, PAGE 84.

The 21,005-ct. Brazilian Princess, the world's largest faceted blue topaz, cut from a 34 kg (75 lb.) crystal and nearly flawless, PAGE 85.

A superb bicolored elbaite crystal group, high from Tourmaline Queen Mine in Pala, California, PAGE 91.

A cluster of bicolored elbaite crystals from Nuristan, Afghanistan, PAGE 99.

208.65-ct. brilliant-cut zircon from Thailand (the largest known blue zircon on public display), PAGE 103.

A group of peridots from Burma and Zabargad Island, PAGE 106.

Polished lapis lazuli boulder from Afghanistan, PAGE 114.

Decorated lapis lazuli elephant carving from the celebrated Fabergé workshop, PAGE 117.

Pendant set with Australian opals and other gems, PAGE 121.

The great 215.85-ct. Harlequin Prince opal, found in Australia, PAGE 122.

Opalized clam weighing 69 cts., from Australia, PAGE 124.

GEM & CRYSTAL COLLECTIONS

and most people have their own favorites—but the following, all of which are illustrated of the Museum's gem and crystal collections.

Moonstone intaglios of three children carved by the noted engraver Ottavio Negri, PAGE 129.

Vessel with cover and hanging chain, carved from a single piece of mutton-fat nephrite jade during the reign of Chi'en Lung, PAGE 132.

Jadeite figure of Quan-yin, goddess of mercy, carved in China during the nineteenth century, PAGE 137.

Nephrite pi disc from the Ming Dynasty (at burials placed beneath the body of the deceased), PAGE 139.

Finely worked green jadeite incense burner from the reign of Chi'en Lung, PAGE 140.

Rock crystal statue of Atlas supporting the world, carved in Russia during the nineteenth century, PAGE 143.

Horse's head, carved from Russian rock crystal during the nineteenth century, PAGE 148.

Splendid amethysts, weighing 163.50 and 88.20 cts., from the Ural Mountains, PAGE 149.

Onyx clock face, carved with cameo-style female figures, PAGE 156.

Pas de Danse, statuette by G. Tonnelier carved from Uruguayan chalcedony, PAGE 160.

A 4.94-ct. demantoid garnet from Poldenwaja in the Ural Mountains of the Soviet Union, PAGE 164.

Hessonite garnet engraved with the head of Christ, from the Vatican collection, PAGE 168.

Engraved almandine garnet bowl from India, PAGE 168.

Nineteenth-century pyrope garnet jewelry from Bohemia, PAGE 169.

Pearl-and-diamond chrysanthemum brooch made by Tiffany around 1900, PAGE 173.

Shell with cameo depicting the "Chariot of the Muses" (Italian work from the late nineteenth century), PAGE 178.

Fresh-water mussel shell with implanted Buddah figures covered with mother of pearl, PAGE 179.

Amber dress ornament carved in China, PAGE 181.

Amber containing the oldest known bee, from the Cretaceous Period about 80 million years ago, PAGE 182.

Jet frog with turquoise details, from New Mexico, PAGE 186.

A Kunzite crystal from Nuristan, Afghanistan, PAGE 192.

Titanite and a twinned crystal, PAGE 193.

Rhodochrosite gem from Kuruman, South Africa, PAGE 195.

A polished slice of intergrown azurite and malachite, PAGE 198.

A fine malachite carving, PAGE 199.

Tracing the Story of Gems

Archaeology gives the earliest picture; it attempts to tell us when and where each gemstone was used, how it was fashioned, and whether it was traded. Recorded history provides insights into the early naming, classification, and everyday significance of gems but especially the stories that are so fascinating.

Early humans were decorating themselves with shells, pieces of bone, teeth, and pebbles by at least the Upper Paleolithic period (25,000-12,000 B.C.). Most of the stones used in early civilizations were opaque and soft with bright colors or beautiful patterns. Carnelian and rock crystal beads were fashioned at Jarmo in Mesopotamia (Iraq) in the seventh millennium B.C. Engraved cylinder seals appeared about two thousand years later in soft stones such as steatite and marble. Their practical function was as a means of identifying goods; when they were rolled on damp clay, a unique imprint resulted. Seals represent a significant level of technical achievement, and they were also valued as adornment and possibly a symbol of status. By the late fourth millennium in the Near East, cylinder seals were made from rock crystal quartz, a hard gemstone, in addition to the soft stones. A woman's belt from the end of the third millennium B.C. was found in Harappa, an ancient center of Indus civilization, decorated with colorful, opaque stones—red carnelian, green steatite, agate, jasper, amazonite, jade, and lapis lazuli—it represents the wealth of gems then available.

Manchu headdress pendant with Imperial jadeite, pearls, sapphires, and pink tourmalines.

ACTIVE EXPLOITATION OF THE LAPIS LAZULI MINES IN Badakshan, Afghanistan, and the turquoise mines on the Sinai Peninsula began around 5,000 years ago; and long-distance trade in gems developed. Lapis lazuli from Badakshan reached Egypt before 3000 B.C. and Sumer (Iraq) by 2500 B.C. China, India, Greece, and Rome received gemstones from the same source. By around the second millennium, Phoenician sea merchants were trading Baltic amber on the coasts of North Africa, Turkey, Cyprus, and Greece. Recent spectroscopic studies of amber beads discovered in Peloponnese graves of Mycenaean Greece (1450 B.C.) confirmed the assumption of their Baltic origin. Trade between the East and West expanded in the fourth century B.C. after the time of Alexander the Great (356-323 B.C.), resulting in an increase in the number of gemstones available.

In all civilizations, magical powers have been ascribed to gems—perhaps out of a need to explain their rarity, beauty, and strangeness in a confusing world. Color played a great role in the symbolism: gold for the sun; blue for the sky, heaven, or sea; red for blood; black for death. Colors were also associated with the planets and astrology—gems became connected here as well. Durability was also important—the unsurpassable hardness of diamond reflects in the belief that it will bring its wearer strength and invincibility. Gems have served as talismans, offering protection, preserving health, and securing wealth, love, and good luck. Of the 143 pieces of jewelry discovered on the mummy of Tuthankhamen (reigned 1361-1352 B.C.)—made of gold, carnelian, jasper, lapis lazuli, turquoise, obsidian, rock crystal, alabaster, amazonite, and jade—a few showed no sign of wear. Given the preoccupation of ancient Egyptian culture with the afterlife, these few were fashioned as amulets to avert evil and bring good luck after death. The others were worn during his lifetime and served as both adornments and talismans. The Babylonians (in contrast to the Egyptians) were not as concerned with life after death. Many of their engraved cylinder seals may have been primarily talismans worn for protection during life.

Written records provide an extensive overview of how gems have been perceived by their owners and users. George F. Kunz, in *The Curious Lore of Precious Stones*, has documented the evidence carefully. In her *Magical Jewels of the Middle Ages and the Renaissance*, jewelry historian Joan Evans offers a wealth of information through studies and translations of ancient literature, surviving inventories of jewelry (some of which note magical powers), and even court records. In one case, she writes: "One of the counts of the indictment of the Chief Justiciar Hubert de Burgh in 1232 was that he had furtively removed from the royal treasury a gem which made its wearer invincible in battle and had bestowed it upon his sovereign's enemy Llewellyn of Wales."

The supernatural powers of gems were regarded either as intrinsic virtues of the stones themselves or were attributed to figures, sigils, or magical inscriptions engraved upon them. These virtues were enumerated in the mineralogical and medical treatises of the time, known as lapidaries.

Medicinal powers of gems were first recorded in Western literature by the Greeks. These virtues, as well as astrological symbolism, were also recorded in Arabic lapidaries and, starting in the eighth century, in European lapidaries influenced by the Arabic works. In medieval Europe, gems were commonly worn as medicinal amulets or taken as potions. Before Pope Clement VII died in 1534, he had taken as medicine powdered gems valued at 40,000 ducats. Robert Boyle (1627-1691), a great advocate of experiment in natural history and author of *Some Considerations Touching the Usefulnesse of Experimental Natural Philosophy*, wrote: "I think, in Prescriptions made for the poorer sort of Patients, a Physician may well substitute cheaper ingredients in the place of these precious ones, whose Virtues are not so unquestionable as their dearnesse."

Throughout the chapters that follow, there will be mention of the chroniclers and their lapidaries. The first important references in Western literature are from the Greek Theophrastus (c. 372-287 B.C.), the successor of Aristotle. In his book *On Stones*, the oldest surviving mineralogy textbook, he described 16 minerals grouped as metals, earths, and stones (the last including gemstones). This classification remained unchallenged until the eighteenth century. He identified as physical properties color, transparency, luster, fracture, hardness, and weight and also noted the medicinal values of gems. Damigeron also wrote an early lapidary in Greek; the text was translated into Latin somewhere between the first and sixth centuries. Pliny the Elder (A.D. 23-79) compiled the knowledge of his predecessors and contemporaries to produce his 37-volume *Historia Naturalis*.

Ancient and modern carvings from China and Japan including rutilated Brazilian quartz sphere and fu dog; nephrite pi disc; lapis junk; serpentine box; yellow serpentine vase; carnelian vase; agate guppy; malachite vase; and an aquamarine-like glass vase.

Volume 37 deals with precious stones and includes "1,300 facts, romantic stories and scientific observations" about sources, mining, use, trade, and the values of gems; gem enhancements; and gem imitations. Pliny's work was influential in Europe well into the Middle Ages. Marbode, bishop of Rennes, composed his elegant lapidary in Latin hexameter in the eleventh century. Although lacking any mineralogical significance, his work is the basis of both medicinal and magical attributes that have been cited by many later writers.

Thirteenth-century works include Volmar's *Steinbüch* as well as the important *De Mineralibus* of Albertus Magnus (1206-1280). This German philosopher noted the magnetic properties of magnetite, experimented with decomposition of arsenic minerals; and described the properties, including magical virtues, of 94 minerals.

Complicating our task of finding out where initial concepts came from is the fact that "borrowing" was not uncommon. Camillus Leonardus's *Speculum Lapidum*, printed in Venice in 1502, was literally translated into Italian and republished as *Trattato delle Gemme* by Ludovico Dolce later in the same century. Another sixteenth-century work, more important than that of Leonardus, is *de Gemmis et Coloribus* by Geronimo Cardano, published in 1587. Anselmus Boetius de Boot, court physician to Holy Roman Emperor Rudolf II, wrote *Gemmarum et Lapidum Historia* (1609); in his extensive work, he provided descriptions of gems and reports on their virtues, although we find the beginnings of doubts as to the infallible powers of gems.

In addition to traditional lapidaries, travel books, such as those by Marco Polo in the thirteenth century and Jean Baptiste Tavernier in the seventeenth, provide information about the use of gems and their sources. Garcia de Orta (1565), Portuguese physician to the viceroy of Goa in India, described diamond mines there, observed mining practices, and reported gems' virtues—he flatly denied a then-commonplace belief that diamond was poison, having seen workers swallow the gem in order to smuggle it.

With the development of empiricism and scientific inquiry in the seventeenth and eighteenth centuries, the study of gemstones as manifestations of a strictly physical universe began. Concepts of chemistry, optics, and crystallography developed along with a desire to categorize so that definitions and tests could begin to differentiate among all objects.

Today we view gems from a very different perspective from that of a few hundred years ago, but we still have much to learn. Color, the great deceiver in the transparent stones, is still a subject filled with questions about specific causes in each gemstone. New gemstones and new treatments of the old are discovered and add to the diversity. The beauty of the challenge is the gems themselves; they offer a wonderfully exciting stimulus for exploring nature.

What Is a Gem?

T he purpose of this chapter is to answer this question and to discuss the attributes that distinguish gems. The rest of the book examines the gemstones; it starts with the traditional "precious" stones, then moves through the colored stones, ending with organic gems, rare and unusual gemstones, and ornamental material. However—aside from the "precious" four: diamond, ruby, sapphire, and emerald—there is neither a system nor agreement on how to order gems, because beauty, their hallmark, is a matter of taste and culture. Pearls, jade, and opal are highly regarded, but ranking them—who knows? Moreover, tastes and availability change with time; today's ranking could be noticeably different in a decade. You undoubtedly have your own favorites, but browse through all the chapters for some beautiful surprises.

Getting back to the title question: to us, a gem is a gemstone that has been fashioned—cut, shaped, and/or polished—to enhance its natural beauty. The gemstone is the raw material or "rough"; the gem is the finished product. Most gemstones are minerals, but some are rocks, and a few are the organic products of once-living animals or plants. A gem ruby is created from a piece of the mineral corundum; lapis and jade are rocks; and pearls, amber, and jet are organic products.

Myriad colored stones, including topaz, amethyst, aquamarine, morganite, chrysoberyl, peridot, smoky quartz, citrine, calcite, rhodochrosite, kunzite, and fluorite; varying from 14.91 to 454 cts.

What Gems Are Made Of

ROCKS AND MINERALS REPRESENT TWO DIFFERENT LEVels of organization of matter. Atoms are the building blocks for minerals; minerals are the building blocks for rocks; and rocks make up the solid Earth. Rocks are physical assemblages of pieces of minerals. The boundaries between all the grains tends to make rocks opaque, so it is usually their color or occasionally their toughness that makes them attractive as gemstones. Minerals are more frequently valued as gemstones because they can be transparent and fashioned into glittering gems. The fact that minerals are crystalline allows them to form large transparent gemstones and have interesting optical properties.

Being crystalline means that a mineral's constituent atoms—one or more of the 92 naturally-occurring chemical elements—are organized in a regular geometric pattern that repeats in three dimensions to form a solid body called a crystal. One usually recognizes a crystal by its natural flat surfaces called *faces*. Crystals can be invisibly small or larger than automobiles, but a crystal's properties and atomic organization are the same throughout the entire body. The geometric arrangement of atoms is called the *crystal structure*. The atoms are linked by chemical bonds—electrical forces and electron interactions between atoms—that literally hold the mineral together and produce its properties. A mineral also has a chemical composition that can be defined within well-constrained limits, usually by a relatively simple chemical formula. Corundum is natural aluminum oxide, Al_2O_3. Each of the roughly 3,000 mineral species is defined by its chemical composition and its crystal structure.

A well-formed crystal is the external expression of the symmetry of the repeating arrangement of atoms within. The way in which shapes are repeated determines the type of symmetry. A crystal with faces that repeat across a plane (a mirror), about an axis (rotation), or through a point (inversion) contains one (or more) elements of these three basic kinds of symmetry. For example, a hexagonal green beryl crystal rotated 60 degrees about its center (axis) appears unmoved; it is repeated by sixfold rotation. Some minerals have no symmetry, and others have many symmetry elements. The symmetry a crystal can possess is constrained by the ways groups of atoms can be repeated in space to create a solid crystal. There are only seven basic systems of crystal symmetry, which are shown diagrammatically. All minerals belong to one of these seven crystal systems. The crystal symmetry is not only helpful in identification, as with the hexagonal beryl, but properties such as hardness and color can vary with direction in the crystal, depending upon its symmetry. Thus, a gem is cut from an individual crystal to take advantage of not only its uniformity as a transparent, cohesive object but, possibly, its special directionally-dependent properties.

Mineral crystals are created by growth from a nucleus, some speck or mineral surface, by additions of successive layers of atoms on the crystal's outer surface. Some minerals, particularly tourmaline among gemstones, manifest this layered growth with concentrically color-banded crystals. Growth occurs when the temperature, pressure, and chemical environment are favorable; but most mineral crystals, such as the grains in rocks, do not have symmetric form with flat faces because the crystals grow into or against one another. Well-formed crystals are rare because they need not only appropriate and sustained growing conditions but also a space in which to grow, such as a cavity, where growth will be unimpeded. Even then, perfectly symmetrical crystals are rare.

The term *habit* refers to the actual shape of a mineral crystal or aggregate. For example, a common habit for crystals is the prism, a form with parallel sides that looks like an extruded polygon. Most pencils, like beryl crystals, have the form of a hexagonal prism. Some minerals, such as chrysoberyl, grow as multiple crystals, known as *twins*. Two or more crystals develop in intimate contact, as an "intergrowth," and give the appearance of a single crystal with more symmetry than the mineral possesses, such as manifesting a sixfold rotation axis where there is none. Other minerals form fine-scale, rocklike aggregates, such as nephrite jade or the jasper form of quartz. A mineral's habit may vary, depending on the conditions during crystal growth.

Minerals are said to form a *group* if they share the same crystal structure—the atoms have the same arrangement, but the chemical elements vary. Garnet is a mineral group with many members. Two gemstone members in the garnet group are spessartine, $Mn_3Al_2Si_3O_{12}$, and almandine, $Fe_3Al_2Si_3O_{12}$. Because the size of manganese (Mn) and iron (Fe) atoms are similar, a continuum of mineral compositions between spessartine and almandine is possible. This phenomenon, called *solid solution*, is important to diversity (and complexity) in gemstones like the garnets.

A color or compositional variant of a mineral is termed a *variety*; e.g., emerald is a green variety of beryl. Many of the appellations associated with gems are variety rather than mineral names.

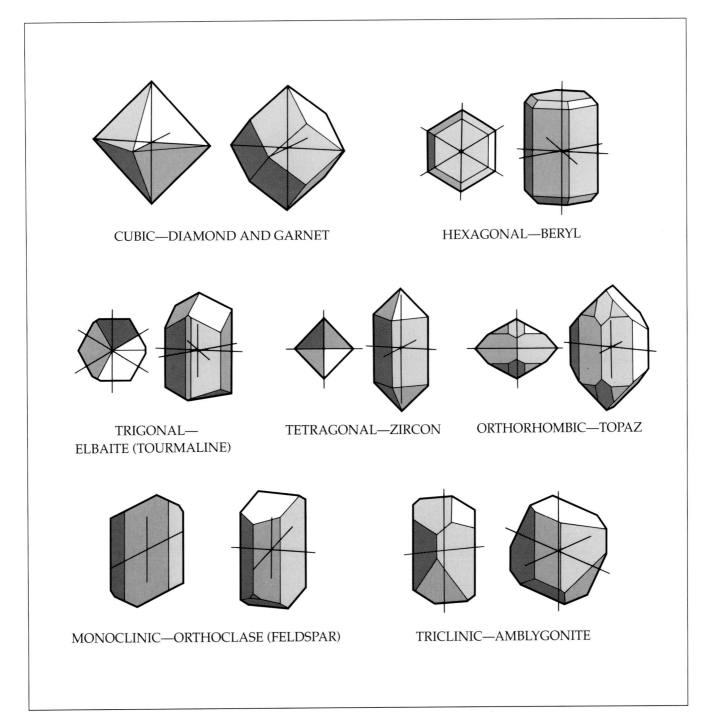

CUBIC—DIAMOND AND GARNET

HEXAGONAL—BERYL

TRIGONAL—
ELBAITE (TOURMALINE)

TETRAGONAL—ZIRCON

ORTHORHOMBIC—TOPAZ

MONOCLINIC—ORTHOCLASE (FELDSPAR)

TRICLINIC—AMBLYGONITE

The Crystal Symmetry Systems: The combination of symmetry and repetitive organization of atoms produces only seven basic geometries for defining crystals. The diagrams show a crystal and axes for gem minerals in each of the seven crystal systems.

Important Gem Properties

THE MOST SIGNIFICANT CHARACTERISTIC OF A GEM-stone is its visual beauty; after this come durability and rarity, but without beauty, the others mean little. The beauty of ruby, emerald, and turquoise lies in magnificent, intense colors, while that of diamond is the complete absence of color combined with high brilliance. Flawless transparency is critical for the beauty of diamond, aquamarine, and topaz, while inclusions account for the presence of a star in ruby and sapphire and the cat's eye. The lively play of color in opal and the pleasing iridescence in labradorite are unique for these gems, as are the numerous patterns in agate. To understand what gives a gem its most important characteristic, visual beauty, we need to examine the ways in which a mineral interacts with light.

Light, Vision, and Color

The source of color is light, its interaction with an object, and our ability to perceive the result. The color we see is the light that is reflected or transmitted and not absorbed. The causes of color in gemstones are many and varied.

If a mineral's color is inherent, it is called *idiochromatic*, "self-colored." Malachite, copper carbonate, is always green because copper causes the color and is intrinsic to the mineral.

Minerals that owe their color to physical effects, such as internal boundaries and contaminants, are called *pseudochromatic*, "false-colored." Jasper, a form of quartz with extremely fine grain size, can contain small particles of iron oxide particles (hematite) that make it brick red. Physical scattering of light, described a little later, produces the play of colors in precious opal.

Allochromatic, "other-colored," minerals are generally colorless and transparent in their pure state but develop color with minor changes in crystal composition or from structural imperfections. Such gemstones are the most numerous, intriguing, and difficult to identify by color alone. Substitution of certain transition elements for aluminum in corundum yields a variety of colors: some iron and titanium causes blue sapphire; a little iron alone results in yellow sapphire; a little chromium produces ruby. (Transition elements are chemical elements in the middle of the periodic table whose electron energy transitions can be stimulated by visible light, thus yielding color.) The same element can result in different colors; a minor substitution of chromium for aluminum in colorless beryl produces the spectacular emerald. Other transition elements important in causing color are manganese, copper, and vanadium.

Damage and/or mistakes in the crystal can cause color. Smoky quartz is the result of radiation damage to the crystal. It can be produced by naturally-occurring radioactive minerals adjacent to a quartz crystal or by bombardment with subatomic particles from a nuclear reactor.

Color in some crystals changes with their orientation; the phenomenon is called *pleochroism,* "more coloring." Sapphires and rubies and pink

(Opposite) Gemstone crystals including tourmaline, aquamarine, morganite, heliodor, topaz, kunzite, spodumene and citrine.

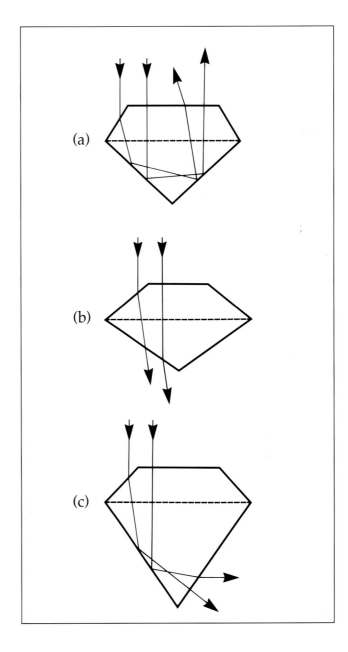

(Right) A gem properly proportioned with respect to its refractive index will reflect back the light that enters it (a), yielding maximum brilliance. Light "leaks" out of a gem cut too shallow (b) or too deep (c), diminishing brilliance.

spodumene are more deeply colored when viewed down the prism axis. Tourmaline gems can have two different colors, depending upon the direction you look through the gem or crystal. Orientation is very important to the appropriate fashioning of pleochroic gemstones.

A few gems, notably the ruby, have the property of fluorescence; they can absorb blue and ultraviolet light and reradiate some of the energy in a redder portion of the spectrum. The result is a more intense color with an extra glow that dazzles the eye.

Gems' Sparkle

Another important pair of related optical properties of a gem is the way it reflects and refracts light. Luster is the reflection or scattering of light from a gem's surface; it can range from metallic to vitreous to resinous to earthy. High luster requires both a smooth surface and a high reflectivity. Polishing of all gems is important in part to improve luster.

Brilliance, on the other hand, is the reflection of light from inside a faceted gem. ("Life" and "liveliness" are used synonymously for brilliance.) This quality is a function of both the cut and the refractive index (R.I.). The R.I. is actually a measure of the velocity of light in the gemstone but is manifested by the degree to which light is bent when entering a substance at an angle and the critical angle at which light is reflected instead. The angles of cut, and thus a gem's proportions, are specifically gauged to the R.I. of each gemstone so that the faceted gem will reflect back from inside the light that enters. All minerals except those of the highest symmetry—cubic—actually have two or three R.I.s and are called "birefringent." Reflectivity is positively correlated with refractive index, and both increase with a substance's density. Thus it is not an accident that the fine transparent gemstones like diamond and sapphire are denser than most minerals. (Density is measured in terms of specific gravity, S.G., the weight of a substance relative to that of an equal volume of water.)

Fire develops in a gem from the phenomenon known as *dispersion*. The component colors in white light are bent to varying degrees during refraction, with the consequent separation of colors into the rainbow. For two different gems of the same size and cut, the one with greater dispersion will display a better spectrum of colors, or fire; the diamond will have better fire than the quartz gem. In colored gemstones, dispersion is usually masked by the predominant color, so that this property becomes unimportant.

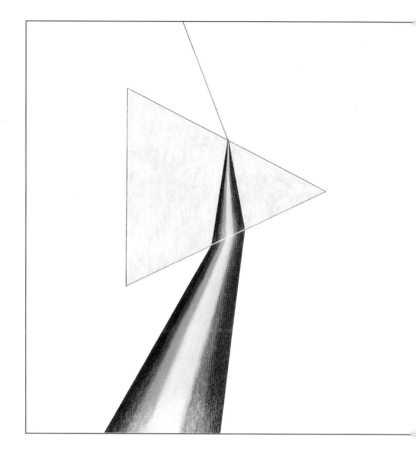

Scattering of Light

Small to submicroscopic features can produce some surprising visual effects in gemstones. Reflections from parallel layers of transparent materials cause pearly luster. The pearl is built up of concentric layers and gives this luster its name. The cat's eye effect, chatoyancy (a literal translation from French), is a band of reflected light that appears in certain gemstones. The cat's eye is produced by many straight parallel fibrous inclusions that scatter light perpendicular to their long direction. In corundum, three directions of needles can occur, yielding multiple chatoyancy in the form of a six-rayed star. This is called *asterism*. The star is visible only when the stone is viewed down the axis of intersection of the inclusions.

Scattering from very small features often imparts colors. In moonstone, thin layers and small elliptical bodies scatter blue light most effectively and yield the characteristic pale blue sheen. Small particles arranged in a periodic pattern will scatter individual colors by optical diffraction, which is observed commonly in bird feathers and butterfly wings. The best example in gemstones is precious opal. A number of other similar scattering phenomena produce colors in stones like fire agate.

White light separates into component colors on passing through (opposite) a glass prism and (above) a colorless gem due to dispersion—the result for the gem is "fire."

Mohs Hardness Scale

1 *Talc*

2 *Gypsum*

3 *Calcite*

4 *Fluorite*

5 *Apatite*

6 *Orthoclase*

7 *Quartz*

8 *Topaz*

9 *Corundum*

10 *Diamond*

Durability

Durability, the most important physical attribute in gauging a gemstone's merit, has three aspects: hardness, toughness, and stability. Hardness is the resistance to being scratched and is literally a measure of the strength of the chemical bonds in a substance. In 1822, German mineralogist Friedrich Mohs proposed a scale of hardness consisting of 10 minerals ranked in order of their ability to scratch one another; 1 is the softest, and 10 is the hardest. The scale is relatively linear; that is, each mineral is nearly one value of hardness greater than the previous one. Diamond, 10, is anomalous; it should have a value more like 100 to show its hardness relative to the others. Diamond is held together with extremely strong chemical bonding.

Quartz, with Mohs hardness of 7, is a common component of dust, so that gemstones softer than 7 are subject to scratching, particularly in rings, where abrasion is commonplace.

Toughness is a gem's resistance to cracking, chipping, and actually breaking. A chief threat to crystals is planes of weakness, representing directions in the crystal structure with relatively fewer or weaker chemical bonds. The result is cleavage—splitting along a plane. Diamond, the hardest mineral, lacks toughness because of its octahedral cleavage planes. Most diamonds in engagement settings will show small chipped corners after years of exposure to everyday wear and tear. Topaz, with a hardness of 8, also lacks toughness. It has one perfect cleavage and therefore is difficult to facet. Some gemstones fracture easily as a result of internal stress, which lowers their strength. Both opals and obsidian can chip easily due to physical or thermal shock. Nephrite jade, with a hardness between 6 and 6.5, is the toughest of gemstones. With a strong interlocking network of fibrous crystals, it can be fashioned into the most intricate shapes. Another tough gem is the pearl; one will not break if dropped on a hard floor, although the gem's hardness is only about 3.

Stability, the resistance to chemical or structural change from deteriorating forces, is an important factor in a gemstone's durability. Opals contain water, and some lose it in dry air; the result is cracks, or crazing, from loss of volume. Pearls are damaged by acids, alcohol, and perfume. Porous gemstones like turquoise can pick up oils and coloring from the skin. The color of some kunzite and amethyst fades on exposure to sunlight. However, the majority of gems are stable in most conditions the wearer is likely to place them.

Where Gems Come From

GEMSTONES ARE UNCOMMON IN THE MINERAL KINGDOM and require unusual geological conditions for their creation. They can form at various depths within the Earth's crust or even below in the mantle. All three classes of rock-forming environments—igneous, metamorphic, and sedimentary—produce gemstones, although the first two are predominant. Important gemstone sources, or occurrences, are gem pegmatites. Crystals that are measured in inches and feet occur in granitic pegmatites. They crystallize from the molten rock, magma, as the final step after a large quantity of granitic rock has already solidified. The residual magma becomes rich in volatiles such as fluorine, boron, lithium, beryllium, and water. The volatiles promote the growth of large crystals and are also components of aquamarines, tourmalines, and topaz, for example. The pegmatites of Minas Gerais in Brazil, the Ural Mountains of the Soviet Union, the Malagasy Republic, and San Diego County, California, are remarkable for their gem-quality crystals.

Another environment in which gemstones are found that has nothing to do with their original formation is placers or alluvial (river) deposits. Minerals released by weathering of rocks exposed at the Earth's surface wash into rivers (and onto beaches), where they concentrate as gravels; less durable minerals break up and wash away. Dense minerals are most effectively concentrated in this way. Alluvial gemstones are often superior to those found in solid rock because only the strongest, most perfect specimens survive the abrasive transport.

Gems and the Market

Practical questions also determine which minerals and rocks can be used as gems. Does a gemstone occur in pieces of sufficient size to fashion a reasonable gem? Many minerals could be used as gems if they occurred in clear crystals weighing several carats. Olivine is a common mineral, but geological occurrences of the green peridot crystals of adequate size are rare.

To be commercial, the gemstone abundance must be sufficient to underwrite the cost of developing a demand. Inadequate supply leads to unviable economics. Today the issue is often the depletion of sources. Alexandrites were never plentiful, but now the supply is so scarce that few examples ever reach the mass market. Consequently, even with a spectacular, though short-lived, find at Lavra de Hematita in Brazil in 1987, alexandrite is almost unknown except by collectors and gem experts.

Is a gemstone sufficiently rare to have status? Because gems are often the hallmark of social status and wealth, a degree of rarity is important. A gemstone may not lose its appeal with overabundance, but its value will certainly be affected.

CARAT, THE STANDARD UNIT OF MASS FOR GEMS

The abbreviation for carat is ct.

1 ct. =	*0.2 grams*	
5 cts. =	*1.0 grams*	= *0.035 ounce (Avoirdupois)*
141.75 cts. =	*28.35 grams*	= *1 ounce*

Do not confuse carat with karat, the unit of measure of gold purity. Both terms probably originate from the Middle Eastern word for the seed of the carob tree (Arabic quirat). The seeds have remarkably uniform weight and were used to balance the scales in the ancient markets.

Evaluating Gems

EVALUATION OF GEMS IS A SEARCH FOR AND COMPARISON with perfection. There is a great range in qualities of some properties in each gemstone and no absolute code by which to compare different gems.

Color. A fine colored gem must have a good depth of color, not so pale as to be uncertain and not so deep as to appear black. Different color saturation can mean a remarkable difference in the price of two gems. The color should be uniform, not blotchy or strongly zoned. For some gemstones like amethyst, finding uniformity is the most serious problem in locating a fine sample. In multicolored gemstones, sharp, straight boundaries to color change are important rather than uniformity.

Clarity. This characteristic is important in most gems, less so in others. Two varieties of beryl have very different limits to what is acceptable. A fine aquamarine should be virtually without flaw, but a fine emerald will almost certainly have a few small inclusions. In fact, an emerald free of inclusions is suspected of being synthetic. Flawless transparency—freedom from inclusions and cracks—is critical to the beauty of gems like diamond and topaz.

Weight. The weight of a gem is always a factor in determining price. The value of ruby, diamond, and emerald increases dramatically with weight because large crystals are rare. This increase is an actual rise in the price per carat. Topaz, aquamarine, and rock crystal increase far less in value with increasing size because large crystals of these gemstones are relatively abundant. When a stone exceeds the size where it can be readily set in a piece of jewelry, its unit price plateaus or even begins to fall.

Cutting and Polishing. For an opaque gemstone, only the surface properties are important. Such stones are rarely faceted and are more frequently polished to obtain a smooth, rounded surface. The cabochon ("bald head"), a rounded top usually with a flat base, is used for translucent and opaque gemstones and gems displaying

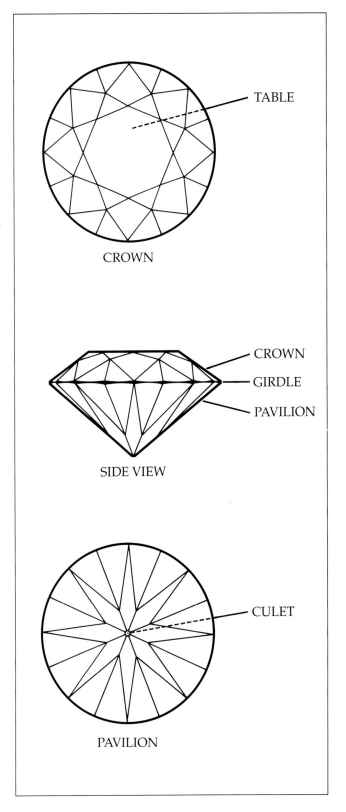

The names for the various portions and facets of a cut stone diagrammed for a round brilliant.

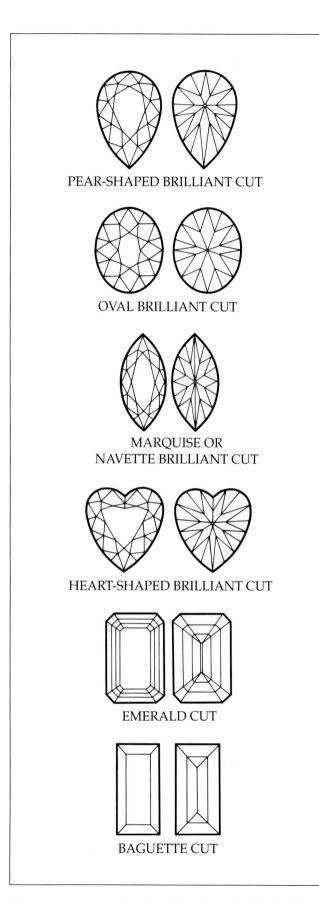

PEAR-SHAPED BRILLIANT CUT

OVAL BRILLIANT CUT

MARQUISE OR
NAVETTE BRILLIANT CUT

HEART-SHAPED BRILLIANT CUT

EMERALD CUT

BAGUETTE CUT

*Some popular gem cuts, viewed from the table (top) and
pavilion (bottom)*

optical phenomena such as chatoyancy, asterism, and play of color.

Transparent gemstones are faceted. The process consists of cutting with an abrasive (usually diamond) saw, grinding with abrasives, and polishing facets. Cut also means the shape or style in which a gem is fashioned. Faceting and proper proportioning are essential for revealing the full beauty of transparent minerals, particularly a diamond's fire. Diamond faceting first appeared in the fourteenth century, but intense study of methods was stimulated by the great nineteenth-century discoveries of diamonds in South Africa. We now know the exact angles which must be present between facets to cause all light incident on the gem to be completely reflected for maximum brilliance. The round brilliant cut with its modifications (oval, pear, marquise, and heart) and the step (emerald) cut are the most popular.

The quality of cutting and polishing is another factor in the evaluation of all gems, although particularly significant for diamond. Many dealers will buy poorly faceted or proportioned stones and have them recut with reduction in weight but dramatic increase in value.

Gem Enhancement. During the last decade, enhancement of gemstones by chemical and physical means has become very common. Irradiation is being used to enhance or change the color of many stones. For some gems, chemical treatment or impregnation is used; procedures include bleaching, oiling, waxing, plastic impregnations, and dyeing. Heat treatment improves the color and clarity of some gems. Not all types of treatment can be detected at present. In 1989, a resolution was adopted by the members of the International Colored Gemstone Association for disclosure of gemstone enhancement upon request by customers.

Gem Substitutes. Substitutes are substances that so resemble a gemstone's properties that mistaken identity can occur. A relatively inexpensive gemstone may be substituted for a more valuable one, such as citrine quartz substituted for precious topaz. This practice is fraudulent.

Man-made substitutes fall into two categories: synthetics and simulants. A synthetic is the exact same substance as the natural mineral but grown in the laboratory. Synthetic gemstones have been produced commercially since the end of the nineteenth century; the first was synthetic ruby. Initially, there was fear that less expensive synthetics would dilute the market for natural stones and, thus, reduce the latter's value; this has never occurred. Distinguishing the natural from the synthetic gem is not always easy. Natural stones usually contain some inclusions that aid identification, whereas synthetics sometimes manifest evidence, such as lines and bubbles, of their synthesis. Very sophisticated techniques may be required to differentiate the nearly perfect natural gem and the synthetic.

Simulants usually have no natural counterpart but have optical properties that closely resemble those of a natural gem. Cubic zirconia—zirconinum oxide—is so inexpensive, so readily available, and so resemblant of diamond that it has replaced virtually all previously used diamond simulants.

Imitation gems have been in use since antiquity. They may be glass, plastic, or composite stones consisting of two (doublets) or three (triplets) parts. These parts may be genuine, imitation, or both. A clever imitation of Imperial jade is a triplet made of a hollow, colorless jadeite cabochon filled with a green jellylike substance cemented to a flat jadeite back. The color is magnificent but eventually disappears when the green substance dries. Opal is commonly made in doublets and triplets that utilize thin seams of the gem material and at the same time protect this fragile gem. Except in the instance of opal, composite stones generally have been replaced by synthetics.

Several examples of composite gems: (1) Opal doublet; (2) Soudé emerald doublet; (3) Garnet doublet; (4) A triplet; and (5) A jadeite triplet.

(1) PRECIOUS OPAL / COMMON OPAL, CHALCEDONY, OR GLASS

(2) GREEN CEMENT / ROCK CRYSTAL / ROCK CRYSTAL

(3) GARNET / GLASS

(4) ROCK CRYSTAL / COLORED GLASS / ROCK CRYSTAL

(5) WHITE JADEITE / GREEN JELLYLIKE SUBSTANCE / WHITE JADEITE / WHITE JADEITE

Diamond

Diamond is the ultimate example of a gemstone with dual values. On the one hand, it is the peerless model for the colorless gem with its superior brilliance and fire and, on the other, it is the hardest of all substances; only diamond abrasive can fashion a diamond. Diamond as an ancient gem with magical properties is tied to India, its earliest source. There its hardness was appreciated, but the wellspring for diamond's value was the magical virtues that were believed to derive from the crystal form and optical properties—the ideal stone was a clear, transparent, fiery octahedron. The octahedron is the only crystal habit of diamond that manifests the "dazzling division of colors" that epitomizes the mineral's ideal high dispersion. Although diamond octahedra are not uncommon, ones that are sufficiently perfect to show fire are a rarity. This problem of scarcity in obtaining "perfection" might have been solved by reshaping (cleaving and polishing) poorly formed diamonds to bring out their sparkle and improve octahedral form. However, any alteration of a diamond was taboo, destined to destroy its magical properties. It is a wonder that the connection of fiery optics to the popularly perceived magical virtues was ever made.

Naturally-colored diamonds from the Aurora collection from sources around the world. (On loan from Aurora Gems, Inc.)

Properties

DIAMOND'S HARDNESS IS PRODUCED BY THE EXTREME-ly strong chemical bonds each carbon extends to four adjacent neighbors. This configuration yields a crystal structure of high symmetry as expressed by octahedron- and cube-shaped crystals. However, one direction in the structure is crossed by relatively few bonds, which results in a perfect cleavage plane that repeats via symmetry to define an octahedron. Diamonds are routinely split along this cleavage to form smaller pieces for cutting gems. Cleavage is also diamond's main failing as a gemstone—a faceted stone can break or chip. Other results of diamond's strong and compact structure are a relatively high density, high refractive index, and high dispersion. These two optical properties give diamonds their ideal brilliance and fire.

We usually think of diamonds as colorless gems, but most are slightly to noticeably yellowish. Intense, attractive colors like canary yellow, pink, green, blue, purplish, and the rare red are called "fancy" colors. Color is due to the presence and distribution of minor amounts of nitrogen (most yellows) or boron (blues) in diamond crystals. Defects and radiation damage also contribute to color; several colors can be produced by artificial irradiation, sometimes followed by heat treatment. A bluish daylight fluorescence is relatively common in diamonds, and fancy colored stones are renowned for their spectacular range of fluorescence in ultraviolet light.

Chemically diamond is pure carbon, the same as graphite, a soft mineral used in pencils. The dramatically different properties of the two minerals are caused by the chemical bonding of carbon atoms—all strong bonds in diamond, some weak ones in graphite. Diamonds are extremely stable under ordinary conditions but—unlike other crystalline gemstones—when heated red hot in air, will literally vanish to form carbon dioxide.

DIAMOND DATA

Carbon:	C
Crystal symmetry:	Cubic
Cleavage:	Perfect in four directions, defining an octahedron
Hardness:	10
Specific gravity:	3.514
R.I.:	2.417 (high), superb brilliance
Dispersion:	High, superb fire

(See pages 22–29—"What Is a Gem?"—for explanation of data and definition of terms.)

A large 25-ct. octahedral diamond crystal in kimberlite from the Premier Mine, Kimberley, South Africa. (On loan from Mrs. Charles W. Engelhard.)

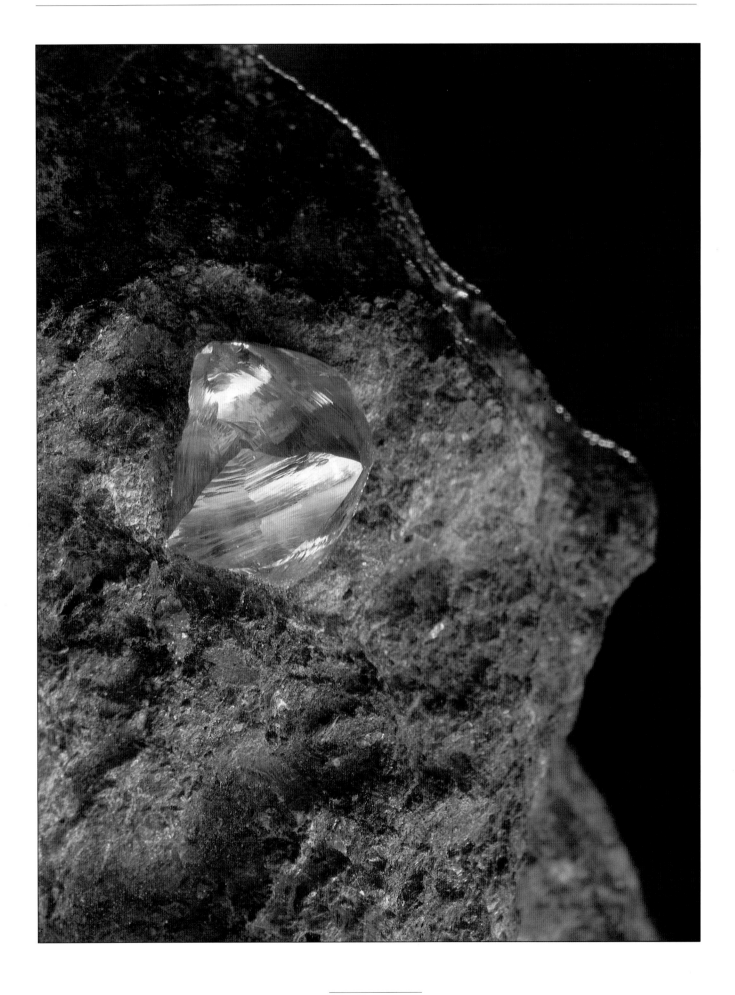

Historic Notes

Diamonds were revered and highly valued as talismans as far back as 800 B.C. in India, and for more than twenty-five centuries, that country was the only supplier of the gemstone. Diamonds and their reputation for metaphysical powers arrived in Rome around the first century B.C. Pliny describes this substance that will scratch all others, confirming the name for the hardest of substances—*adamas*. The word is Greek, meaning "I tame" or "I subdue," and well suits diamond's hardness.

During the first century A.D., prominent Romans wore uncut diamonds set in gold rings as talismans, and leading figures were awarded diamonds by the emperor; specimens of the period are yellowish or brownish, possibly indicating that India's best stones were not exported and almost certainly that the stones available were worn for their powers rather than their beauty.

According to Pliny, diamonds were known only to kings; indeed, very few kings possessed them even as late as the thirteenth century. Louis IX of France (1214-1270) issued an order forbidding women, including queens and princesses, to wear them. Agnes Sorel, the mistress of King Charles VII (1422-1450) dared to wear diamonds, and she is credited with popularizing them in the French court. During the second half of the century, the gem was more frequently worn but only by royalty. The first diamond engagement ring was given to Mary of Burgundy by Hapsburg Emperor Maximilian I in 1477.

Louis XIV of France (1638-1715), the Sun King, collected many fine-quality diamonds. Jean Baptiste Tavernier, jeweler, merchant, and traveler, was influential in bringing diamonds to the court's attention. He made six trips to the Orient, visited Indian diamond mines, and brought back fabulous stones.

Cutting began in the fourteenth century in India and Europe, and diamond became a gem in the modern sense, treasured for its sparkling beauty. During the eighteenth century, diamonds became gems "par excellence," although exclusively for the super rich. Monarchs maneuvered for possession of them; the histories of famous and notable diamonds read like adventure stories and fairy tales.

Diamond production in India began to wane in the eighteenth century, but in 1725, diamonds were discovered at Tejuco in Brazil, and the town was renamed Diamantina. Other deposits were found, and Brazil became the world's major supplier. Toward the end of the nineteenth century, Brazilian production waned, and a series of events changed the diamond world dramatically.

Erasmus Jacobs' son found a diamond the size of a marble on the De Kalk farm near the Orange River in South Africa in 1866. It was the first diamond to be found in South Africa and was appropriately named "Eureka." After several other discoveries, a diamond rush began. In 1871, the De Beer brothers discovered diamonds on their farm, and the Kimberley mine began production in what proved to be the richest deposit ever found. Unmechanized mining produced a huge crater known as "The Big Hole." Bucket load by bucket load, 25 million tons of earth were excavated to recover about 3 tons of diamonds.

In 1888, De Beers Consolidated Mines, Ltd., was formed by Cecil Rhodes, who consolidated the unwieldy claims at Kimberley, thus establishing the De Beers monopoly. (More than 100 years later, De Beers still has the monopoly and, through its Central Selling Organization, controls 80 percent of the wholesale market.) A host of diamond discoveries have taken place in this century in Africa, the Soviet Union, China, and Australia.

With these nineteenth- and twentieth-century discoveries, diamonds have reached a popularity never before enjoyed. Ownership of the gem that until the fifteenth century had been reserved for royalty has become a realistic goal for the average person.

THE KOH-I-NOOR

This magnificent gem has the longest history of all the famous diamonds. In 1304, it was in the possession of the rajahs of Malwa. In 1526, it fell into the hands of the founder of the Mogul dynasty and was passed down the line to all the great Moguls until 1739, when Nadir Shah of Persia invaded India. All of the treasures of the Moguls fell into his hands, except the great diamond. He was told that the emperor had the stone hidden in his turban. So, in accordance with an Oriental custom, he invited his vanquished opponent to a feast where turbans would be exchanged. Later, in private, Nadir Shah unrolled the turban, the gem tumbled out, and Nadir is supposed to have exclaimed, "Koh-i-Noor!" (Mountain of Light) when the stone tumbled to the floor.

Later, a Persian king fled with it to the Sikh court. After the Sikh wars, the gem was taken by the East India Company as part of the indemnity levied in 1849 and was subsequently presented to Queen Victoria. She had the 186-carat gem recut to a 108.93-carat oval brilliant. The Koh-i-Noor, set in the Queen Mother's crown, is on view in the Tower of London.

Legends and Lore

HINDUS DIVIDED DIAMONDS INTO FOUR CATEGORIES according to four major castes; each category brought special good to its possessor: the Brahmin, power, friendship, and wealth; Kshatriya, everlasting youth; Vaisya, success; Sudra, good fortune.

Diamond is protective of its owner, according to a mid-fifth-century Sanskrit manuscript. It wards off serpents, fire, poison, sickness, thieves, flood, and evil spirits. Another Hindu belief was that a flawed stone has quite opposite effects; it could deprive even the god Indra of his highest heaven and could cause lameness, jaundice, pleurisy, and even leprosy.

The virtues of diamond are legion. The stone provided fortitude, courage, and victory in battle, and it stood for constancy and purity and enhanced love between husband and wife. Writing in the fourteenth century, Sir John Mandeville noted that diamond loses its magical power because of the sin of its wearer. Two centuries later, Geronimo Cardano was cautious; whereas diamond might make its owner fearless, fear and prudence might contribute more to well-being and survival, he noted. In addition, he stated that diamond's brilliance irritates the mind just as the sun irritates the eye.

For hundreds of years, the belief that diamonds had gender persisted. Theophrastus (c. 372-287 B.C.) divided each species into male (the dark colored stones) and female (the light colored stones). As late as 1566, François Ruet described two diamonds that produced offspring.

During the Middle Ages, physicians debated whether diamond was a potent poison or an antidote to poison. The poison theory was refuted by Portuguese Garcia de Orta, physician to the viceroy of Goa; in describing the Indian mines in 1565, he noted that slaves working in the mines swallowed diamonds in order to steal them and showed no ill effects.

(Opposite) The Golden Maharaja, a 65.60-ct. diamond, was owned by one of the richest maharajahs when shown at the 1937 World's Fair in Paris and at the 1939 New York World's Fair. The gem was featured in the Morgan Hall from 1976 to 1990 as an anonymous loan.

The Lounsbery diamond necklace, designed by Richard Lounsbery for his wife Vera and executed by Cartier of Paris. The necklace contains over 100 diamonds, fashioned in rose, brilliant, pendaloque, and modified single cuts.

The 14.11-ct. emerald-cut Armstrong Diamond.

Single and twinned diamond crystals; maximum dimension is 1 cm (3/8 in.).

Occurrences

DIAMONDS REQUIRE PRESSURES IN EXCESS OF 50,000 atmospheres to grow. The pressure corresponds to a depth of more than 90 miles (about 150 kilometers), which is within the Earth's upper mantle. Kimberlite, an unusual volcanic rock, is the mantle-sourced host for most diamonds. No kimberlite "volcanos" have erupted in over 60 million years, but if one did, the event would be devastating. A velocity exceeding the speed of sound, 740 miles per hour, is required to bring diamond up from the mantle intact. Kimberlites form somewhat carrot-shaped vertical volcanic vents, called "pipes," near the surface.

Initially, kimberlite weathers into a surface layer of "yellow ground" and a lower layer of "blue ground" that will contain intact diamonds. Further erosion carries diamonds into streams, rivers, and eventually beaches where, due to high density, diamonds become concentrated in placers. Many such deposits were discovered in the search for placer gold.

Australia is presently the world's largest producer of diamonds. It is the major producer of the rare and highly valued pink diamonds as well as much industrial-grade diamond. Its Argyle Mines contain 50 percent of the world's proven reserves.

Africa is the diamond continent. Zaire is the second largest diamond producer and was the first for thirty years, until the mid-1980s. Botswana ranks high in diamond production and is particularly important, since more than 50 percent of its output is of gem quality. Namibia is known for its productive beach placer deposits of diamonds, which are 90 to 95 percent of gem quality. South Africa has dropped from first to fifth place in rough diamond output. The giant Premier Mine has yielded many of the finest and most famous of them. Of the 20 largest diamonds found so far, 10 were mined in South Africa. Other important African sources are Ghana, Sierra Leone, Tanzania, Angola, and Lesotho.

The Soviet Union is also a major diamond producer. The sources are primary, with the richest pipe being the well-known Mir in central Siberia.

India's alluvial deposits were the first ever exploited, and many great historic diamonds were found there. The name Golconda, the ancient source, is synonymous with mine wealth. Indian production declined in the eighteenth century, although there is still some small-scale mining. Brazil and Venezuela are old but presently minor diamond suppliers, and China is a new one.

Evaluation

A DIAMOND'S VALUE DEPENDS ON "THE FOUR C'S": carat weight, color, clarity, and cut.

Carat Weight. A 2-carat diamond costs more than twice as much as two 1-carat diamonds of the same quality and substantially more than four times four 1/2-carat diamonds. This fact is a manifestation of the greater rarity, and value, of larger diamonds.

Color. Absolutely colorless "white" stones are graded on the Gemological Institute of America's color grading scale as D. The letter grades run down from D, E, and F on to S through X, at the bottom, for noticeably yellowish stones. To judge a diamond's color, look at it through its side against a white background. The gem should not be examined in direct sunlight, because fluorescence can mask diamond's true color. The most valued natural fancy diamonds are bright red, but all vivid colors command high prices. Diamonds that are colored by irradiation and heating—green, yellow, golden brown, blue, purple and red—require a disclosure.

Clarity. Most diamonds contain natural inclusions; by international agreement, a diamond is regarded as flawless (FL) if no inclusions are visible to the trained eye through a lens or loupe with tenfold magnification. Increasingly visible inclusions diminish the quality and grade of a stone. Recently, vaporizing inclusions with a laser and filling of cleavages and fractures to reduce their visibility have been reported. Such practices must be disclosed.

Cut. Cutting brings out the full brilliance and fire of a diamond. The diamond should be faceted so that the maximum amount of light entering the stone reflects from the back facets and emerges back through the top. Poorly proportioned stones lose a lot of light through the back facets.

The round brilliant cut was developed for diamond and is most popular, because it displays the most brilliance. The oval, pear, and marquise cuts, which are modified brilliant cuts, appear larger than a round brilliant of the same weight but do not attain the same level of brilliance. The emerald cut, also called the step or trap cut, also yields reduced brilliance and, so, is often used for large flawless diamonds that would be blindingly brilliant if cut round.

SYNTHETIC DIAMONDS AND DIAMOND SIMULANT

Gem-quality synthetic diamonds greater than a carat in size were first made in 1970 but only recently have been grown in commercial quantities. These synthetics have been more expensive than natural diamonds. Cubic zirconia, synthetic zirconium oxide, is now the principal diamond simulant and is produced in both colored and colorless varieties.

(Above) The Tiffany Diamond is a 128.54-ct. canary yellow diamond from Kimberley, South Africa. This superb gem was selected for the firm by George F. Kunz in 1879 and cut in Paris. The stone was featured at the Museum in the exhibit "Tiffany: 150 Years of Gems and Jewelry" in 1988.

Corundum

Sapphire and ruby are the gem varieties of the mineral corundum, but few people anticipate the myriad of colors displayed in these gemstones. Ruby is red, as everyone knows, and sapphire comes in all colors except red: pink, orange, yellow, brown, green, blue, purple, violet, black, and colorless. (Sapphire colors other than blue are termed "fancy" colors.) These are all represented in the Museum as in no other public display—our suite of large sapphires, some exceeding 100 carats, is famous. The huge 563-carat Star of India sapphire is one of the Morgan gifts. Its name suggests a story—one might speculate that, after being mined in Sri Lanka in the sixteenth century, it circulated among the treasuries of Indian potentates. If we only knew the sights this stone may have seen! However, George F. Kunz recorded only this enigmatic statement: "[It] has a more or less indefinite historic record of some three centuries and many wanderings." How the gem came into Kunz's hands is unrecorded, but rumor has it that a royal owner needed cash without publicity. An alternate, but doubtful, story is that Kunz had the stone fashioned in New York City in 1900—so much for romance! No matter, the Star of India is magnificent.

The Star of India, the most famous gem in the Museum—is the largest gem-quality blue star sapphire in the world. The 563.35-ct. stone is nearly flawless and exhibits a perfect star. The almost spherical stone also displays a good star on its back side.

Properties

SPECTACULAR COLORS, COMBINED WITH GREAT DURAbility and reasonable abundance, have made sapphires and rubies important gemstones for centuries. Corundum has a tightly bonded structure that results in high density and great hardness, second only to diamond. The mineral is very stable chemically and essentially has no cleavage.

When aluminum is replaced in corundum by transition elements, the great range of colors in sapphire and ruby are produced. Corundum gems are pleochroic, with colors being more intense when the crystal is viewed down the trigonal axis. Some stones manifest color-change pleochroism from purple to blue or, like alexandrite, from blue green to red.

Titanium is incorporated into the crystal structure of corundum at high temperature and, during slow geologic cooling, it crystallizes separately as fine, silky fibrous inclusions of rutile (TiO_2). The result is chatoyancy that is multiplied by corundum's trigonal symmetry into six- and occasionally twelve-rayed star sapphires or rubies. These inclusions also make the gemstone translucent. Heat treatment "dissolves" the silk back into the corundum structure and generally results in a transparent, more intensely colored stone. We could heat the Star of India and create a fabulous blue cabochon—perish the thought!

Corundum crystals are typically hexagonal prisms that are somewhat tapered, often tabular, and frequently marked with triangular striations on the ends.

The Midnight Star, 116.75 cts., is notable for its deep purple violet color. The stone was found in Sri Lanka.

CORUNDUM DATA

Aluminum oxide:	*Al_2O_3*
Crystal symmetry:	*Trigonal*
Cleavage:	*Poor in one direction*
Hardness:	*9*
Specific gravity:	*3.96-4.05*
R.I.:	*1.76-1.78 (moderate)*
Dispersion:	*Moderate*

GEMSTONE CORUNDUM VARIETIES, COLORS, AND SOURCES OF COLOR

Ruby: *Intense red—chromium*

Sapphire: *Blue—iron + titanium*

Other than blue (called fancy sapphires)

Padparadscha: Orange—chromium + ferric iron

Alexandrite-like: Vanadium

Yellow: Ferric iron (or defects)

Green: Ferrous + ferric iron (and defects)

Colorless: Pure, no substitutions

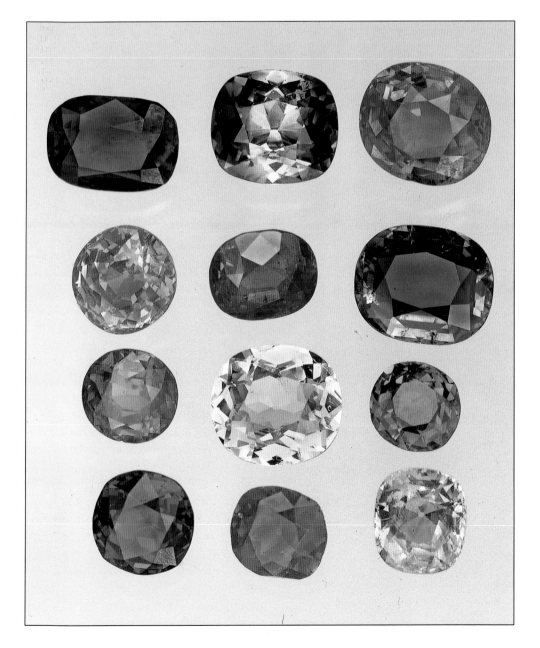

Small Sri Lankan sapphires, ranging from 2.00 to 16.90 cts.

Historic Notes

PRECIOUS STONES WERE GROUPED BY COLOR IN ANTIQ- uity. *Carbunculus* was the Latin term that Pliny the Elder used for transparent red stones. Before 1800, red spinel, red garnet, and ruby were all termed ruby, deriving from the Latin *rubeus,* meaning "red." A number of famous "rubies" have turned out to be spin- els; the Black Prince Ruby, the Timur Ruby, and the Côte de Bretagne Ruby are exam- ples. The Cath- erine the Great Ruby, considered for years to be the largest ruby in Eu- rope, was identified as tourmaline. *Sapphirus* means "blue," and until the Middle Ages, this name was used for lapis lazuli.

The history of sapphire dates back to the sev- enth century B.C., when it was used by ancient Etruscans. Following centuries saw the gemstone used in Greece, Egypt, and Rome. Rome obtained rubies from what is now Sri Lanka and from India, where ruby was the most valued of gems and called "king" and "leader" of precious stones.

Marco Polo's travels took him to the "Island of Serendib" (Sri Lanka), and his thirteenth-century *Book of Marvels* gives high praise to both stones. He tells the story of a Sinhalese king, a ruby, and the Chinese Emperor Kublai Khan. The ruby was huge—4 inches—and Kublai Khan offered an entire city in ex- change for it. The king re- fused, saying that he would not give up his prize for all the treasures in the world. Nothing more is known of this stone, and its report- ed size leads one to speculate whether it really was a ruby.

Sapphire was a fa- vorite stone for rings and brooches of the medieval kings in Europe, and, beginning in the eleventh century, it also became the pre- ferred stone for ecclesiastic rings as well. By the time of the Renaissance, both ruby and sapphire had found favor with the wealthy; indeed, only the wealthy could afford them. Benvenuto Celli- ni, writing in 1560, stated that the price of ruby was eight times that of diamond. And ruby is still generally the most valuable gemstone.

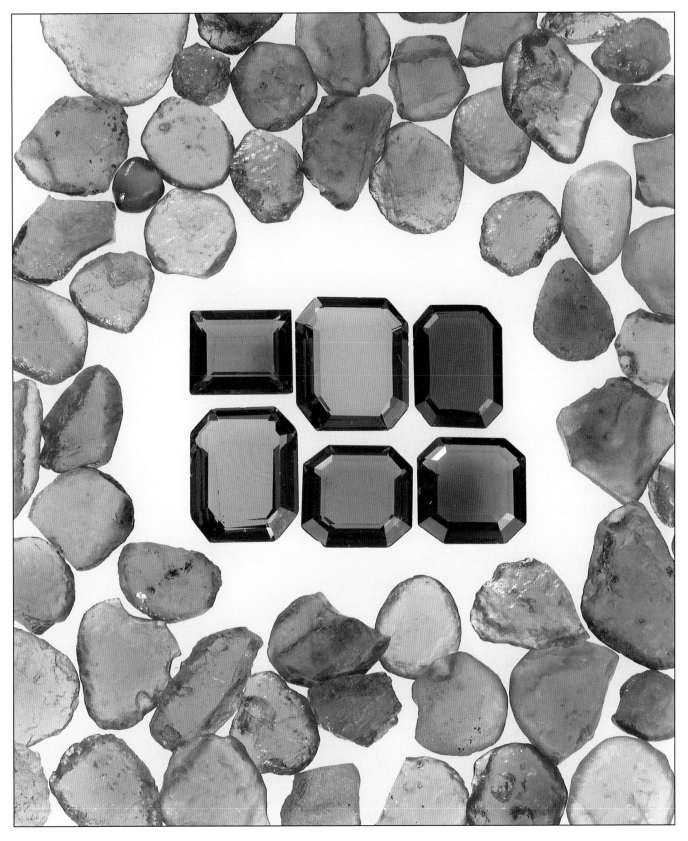

(Above) Typical Montana "Yogo" rough and cut sapphires in blue and violet. The thin tabular gems range from .75 to 2.25 cts. in weight.

(Opposite) The superb 100-ct. Sri Lankan stone is the largest and finest padparadscha sapphire on public display. The varietal name originates from a Sanskrit word for the orangy pink color of the revered lotus.

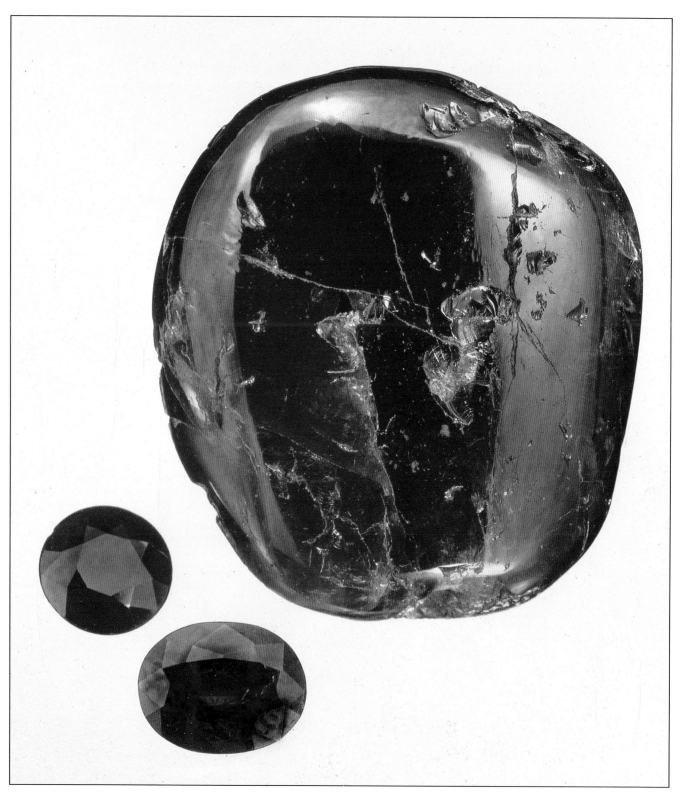

A large Burma ruby cabochon, 47 cts., a round 1.38-ct. ruby from North Carolina, and a 1.87-ct. ruby from Tanzania.

Legends and Lore

THE POWERS THAT HAVE BEEN ASCRIBED TO RUBY OVER the centuries are innumerable. Early Burmese thought the stone would bestow invulnerability when it was actually inserted into the owner's flesh. During the Middle Ages, ruby was believed to have an inner fire that could not be concealed. Camillus Leonardus scorned those who denied the magical powers of precious stones and in the sixteenth century wrote that ruby would preserve its owner's health, remove evil thoughts, control amorous desires, dissipate pestilential vapors, and reconcile disputes. Another belief was that ruby could warn its owner of impending misfortune or calamity by becoming dull and dark. Catherine of Aragon (1485-1536), the first wife of Henry VIII, is said to have foretold her own downfall in perceiving the darkening of her ruby.

Sapphire's powers were equally sweeping. In a treatise ascribed to Damigeron, sapphire protected kings from harm and envy. Its powers included the capacities of banishing fraud and preventing terror, according to Mar-

bode in the eleventh century. Two hundred years later, a French manuscript reported that the stone had the power of preventing poverty, while another lapidary of the same period stated that sapphire makes a stupid man wise and an irritable man good-tempered.

The star sapphire has been called "the stone of destiny"; its three crossed lines represented faith, hope, and destiny. Still another legend refers to these gems as sparks from the Star of Bethlehem. To the Germans, it was "Siegstein," meaning "victory stone," according to De Boot, writing in 1609.

The Hindus, Burmese, and Ceylonese (Sinhalese) recognized a relationship between sapphire and ruby long before the Europeans did. To them, the colorless sapphire was an unripe ruby; if buried in the ground, it would mature and turn red—a belief documented in a sixteenth-century manuscript by Garcia de Orta, the Portuguese physician to the viceroy of Goa. Flawed stones were considered overripe.

A ruby crystal, 4 cm (1 1/2 in.) long, in white marble, from Jagdalak, Afghanistan.

Occurrences

THE PRIMARY SOURCES ARE OF TWO MAJOR TYPES. First, high-temperature metamorphism of claystones and dirty limestones can form all corundum gemstones. Second, sapphires are found in some quartz-free igneous rocks. After weathering from primary sources, corundum gemstones concentrate in placer gravels—the most important commercial deposits.

The earliest sources for both ruby and sapphire are placers in Sri Lanka. Mining began before Buddha's time (624-544 B.C.) near Ratnapura (Sinhalese for "City of Gems"). The rubies found here are paler than Burmese stones. This is the only source of the rare lotus-colored padparadscha sapphire and of the finest star sapphires. The blue sapphires are usually light in color.

Today the world's major sources of rubies are alluvial deposits in Thailand near the Cambodian border. The rubies are mostly dark and brownish red. Dark blue, some green, and only occasionally very fine blue sapphires are also found here.

The world's finest rubies come from the Mogok valley of Upper Burma—the finest deep red (pigeon blood) rubies, occasionally called "Burma rubies" regardless of source, and also very dark or pale rubies. The deposits also yield sapphires and many other gems. The first known record of the Mogok mines is dated A.D. 1496, but indirect evidence suggests much earlier mine operation. The mines' present output is limited.

Australia is the world's largest source of sapphire. In 1987, about 75 percent of the world's output came from New South Wales and Queensland. The sapphires are alluvial, weathered from basalt. The blue stones are generally dark and have an inky appearance.

The major American source of sapphire is Yogo Gulch in Montana, which was discovered in 1895 and has been worked intermittently. The stones are small and waferlike and clear blue to violet. Sapphire gravels occur along the Missouri River near Helena, Montana.

Other important sources of ruby and sapphire are Pakistan, Afghanistan, India, and East Africa.

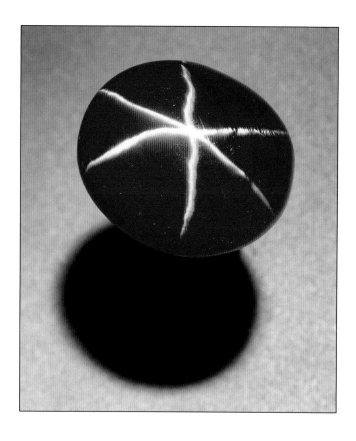

(Above) The DeLong Star Ruby, 100.3 cts., one of the great star rubies, was discovered in Burma during the 1930s and donated in 1938 by Mrs. George Bowen DeLong. In 1964, the ruby was stolen in "The Great Jewel Robbery." Ten months of intricate negotiations involving underworld figures and a ransom of $25,000 followed before the famous ruby was returned.

(Opposite) A fabulous assortment of Sri Lankan sapphires, ranging in weight from 3.50 cts. to 188 cts. The large 112-ct. yellow stone (upper left) is on loan from the Precious Stone Company, New York City.

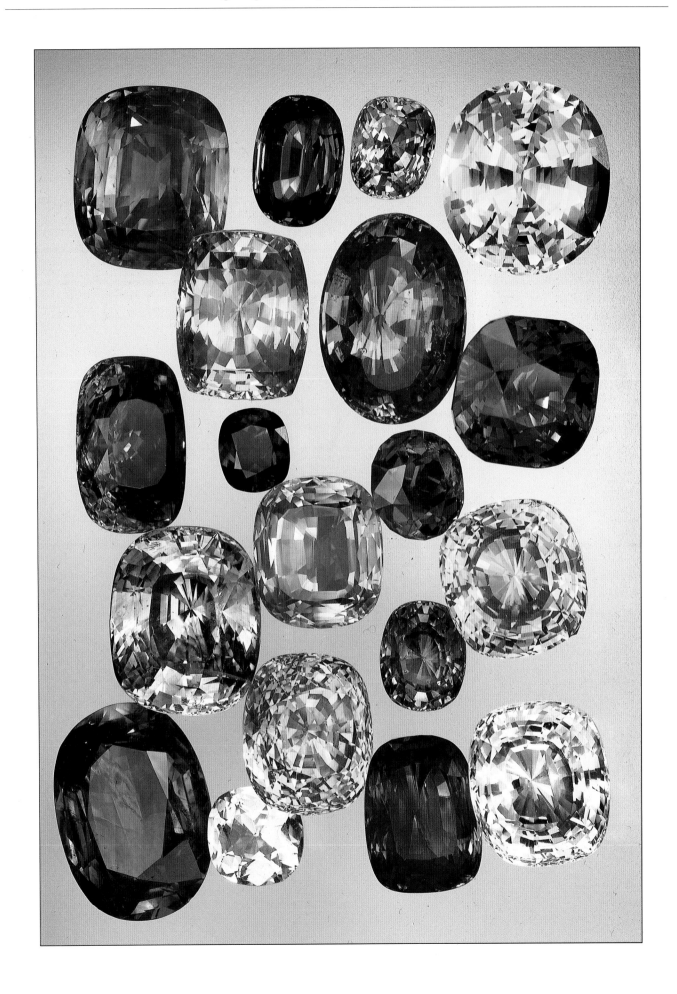

Two intergrown water-worn sapphire crystals, 5 cm (2 in.) long, from Sri Lanka.

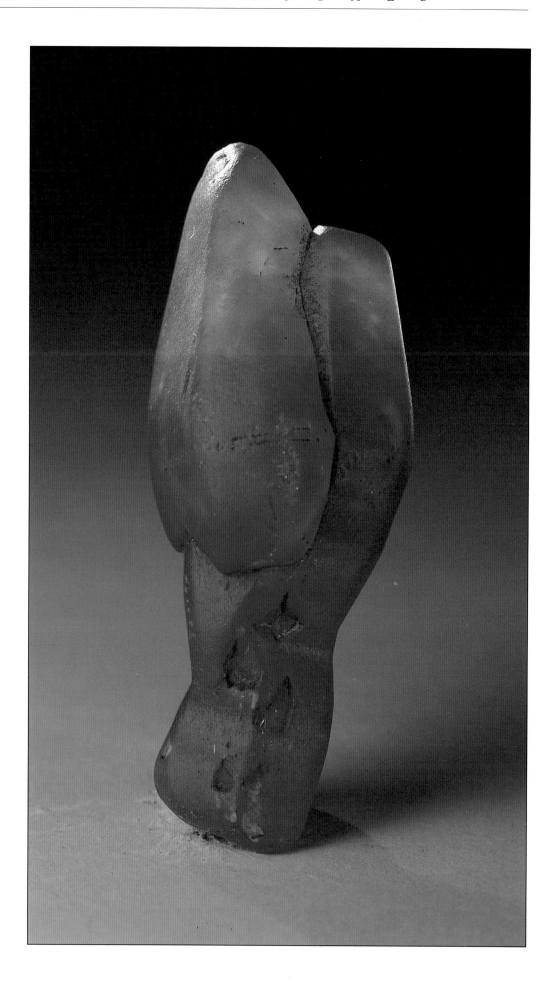

Evaluation

COLOR QUALITY IS MOST IMPORTANT TO RUBIES AND sapphires. Rubies with intense and uniform red to slightly purplish red—the so-called pigeon-blood color—are the most valuable. Medium-deep cornflower-blue sapphires are the most highly prized, and evenness of color is extremely significant. Orange and alexandrite-like sapphire of good quality command very high prices.

Flaws diminish the value of both gems; however, a fine-colored ruby is of high quality even if a minor flaw is present. To improve color and transparency, about 90 percent of new-mined sapphires are heat-treated, with permanent results.

Star rubies and sapphires must be at least translucent to be of gem quality (with the exception of black star sapphires). The star must have well-defined, sharp, straight rays that intersect at the center of the stone.

Large rubies are rarer than large diamonds, emeralds, and sapphires. Thus the value of ruby, even more than of other gems, increases with weight.

Many other gems look like ruby and sapphire and are readily confused with and substituted for them. Synthetic corundums have been on the market since 1902 and are widely used in less expensive jewelry.

GEMSTONES CONFUSED WITH GEM CORUNDUM AND TRADE NAMES

Ruby:	Spinel (Balas ruby), pyrope garnet (Cape and Arizona ruby), red tourmaline (Siberial ruby), and pink topaz (Brazilian ruby)
Blue Sapphire:	Benitoite, cordierite, kyanite, spinel and synthetic spinel, and tanzanite
Green Sapphire:	Zircon
Yellow Sapphire:	Chrysoberyl

Beryl

Beryl is a mineral with several colorful gemstone varieties—aquamarine, morganite, heliodor—but the preeminent one is emerald. A popular misconception is that the Mogul, Ottoman, and Persian emerald treasures come from Oriental deposits. In fact, there are no such sources; these fabulous gems are from Colombian mines, Spanish loot from the New World. Spain needed money and found buyers among the Mogul nobility of India. The Museum's Schettler Emerald is an example; it was cut in India during the period of Mogul domination and probably worn as headgear or a sleeve ornament by a Hindu prince. Its uncut counterpart is the Patricia Emerald. The largest gem-quality crystal on record from the famous Colombian Chivor Mine was discovered in 1920 and sold the following year for $60,000. Only a few large fine crystals have been preserved in museums and bank vaults—emeralds are so valuable as gems that the crystals rarely escape being cut.

The Patricia Emerald is a twelve-sided crystal, 6.6 cm (2 3/5 in.) long, from the Chivor Mine, Colombia, and named for the mine owner's daughter. It weighs 126 grams and is famous for its crystal perfection and superb color as well as its size.

Aquamarine, morganite, and heliodor from various localities, ranging in weight from the 11.38-ct. emerald-cut golden heliodor to the 390.25-ct. aquamarine.

BERYL DATA

Beryllium aluminum silicate:	$Be_3Al_2Si_6O_{18}$
Crystal symmetry:	Hexagonal
Cleavage:	None
Hardness:	7.5-8
Specific gravity:	2.63-2.91
R.I.:	1.566-1.602 (low)
Dispersion:	Low

Properties

BEAUTIFUL COLOR DISTINGUISHES THE BERYL VARIETIES as gemstones. Beryl is a hard mineral but has only moderate brilliance and little fire. Elemental substitutions for aluminum in the crystal structure are the most common sources of color. However, there is a cavity along the sixfold axis in the structure that frequently accepts a chromophoric metal like iron as in the case of aquamarine and some green beryl. Color-zoned crystals are possible, the most interesting being bicolor moganite-aquamarine.

Crystals form distinctive hexagonal prisms that, when from pegmatites, can be among the largest gemstone crystals. Inclusions vary with occurrence and variety. Emeralds are typically heavily flawed with cracks and inclusions of fluids and minerals from rocks in which they grow; these are called "jardin" (garden), the inclusion patterns resembling leaves and branches. The other beryl varieties usually have greater clarity, most commonly containing small parallel fluid-filled tubes that have the appearance of rain when a crystal is strongly illuminated. If these inclusions are fibrous, they can yield chatoyancy in a polished gem.

This Chinese carving of a sitting goddess 10.5 cm (4 1/4 in.) high is the finest and largest morganite carving known.

(Opposite) Well-formed emerald crystal 6.5 cm (2 1/2 in.) long, from Takowaja, Ural Mountains, the Soviet Union.

(Above) Heliodor crystal 10.2 cm (4 in.) in height, from Minas Gerais.

(Right) A platinum pendant set with diamonds and containing an emerald, 1.6 cm (5/8 in.) long.

GEMSTONE BERYL VARIETIES, COLORS, AND SOURCES OF COLOR

Emerald:	*Intense green or bluish green—chromium and/or vanadium*
Aquamarine:	*Greenish blue or light blue—iron*
Morganite:	*Pink, peach, or purple pink—manganese*
Heliodor or Golden beryl:	*Golden yellow to golden green—iron*
Green beryl:	*Light green or too pale to qualify as emerald—iron, chromium, and/or vanadium*
Red beryl or Bixbite:	*Raspberry red—manganese*
Colorless beryl or Goshenite:	*Pure beryl, sometimes with cesium*

Historic Notes

Of the gem beryls, emerald has the longest history. The term *emerald* derives from the Greek *smaragdos*, for which there are conflicting meanings and antecedents. The earliest emeralds, extracted by Egyptians, date from the Ptolemaic era (323-30 B.C.); however, tools dating to Rameses II (c. 1300 B.C.) or even earlier have been found in tunnels at Sikait and Zabara, the location of the emerald mines. These mines were the West's principal source for emeralds until the sixteenth century, although another source was known to the Celts and Romans—Habachtal, south of present-day Salzburg in Austria. (The Archbishop of Salzburg had the deposits worked during the Middle Ages.)

Prior to the Spanish invasions in South America, emeralds from Colombia were traded and prized from Mexico to Chile. Almost from the time of their arrival, the conquistadors observed native rulers wearing them: in 1533 alone, Pizarro sent back four chests of emeralds to Spain. Finding no source in Peru, the Spaniards looked farther north and in 1537 discovered Chivor in what is now Colombia. Following a skirmish with the Muzo Indians, from which the Spanish were forced to retreat, a soldier found an emerald and delivered it to his commander. The Spanish returned in force, defeated the Indians, and took over the Muzo mine. The Colombian gems were larger and of finer quality than any seen in Europe and Asia before the Conquest. They totally supplanted the Egyptian emeralds because of their superior quality.

The histories of aquamarine, heliodor, and morganite are more recent. The first documented use of aquamarine is by the Greeks between 480 and 300 B.C. The gem has been very popular since the seventeenth century. *Heliodor* (golden beryl) derives from two Greek words meaning "sun" and "gift"; this gemstone has also been known since antiquity. It has rarely been used in jewelry, for its color is not outstanding among other yellow gems. Morganite is the latest gem to be recognized in the beryl group. First mined in Madagascar (the Malagasy Republic) in 1902, the gem was named after J.P. Morgan by George F. Kunz.

(Left) Heliodor crystal 7.5 cm (3 in.) long from Siberia in the Soviet Union and a 59.01-ct. cut stone from Sri Lanka.

(Below) A square-cut 278.25-ct. morganite from Minas Gerais in Brazil next to a matrix specimen consisting of a perfect morganite crystal (6.5 cm across) with a gem-quality bicolor elbaite from San Diego County, California.

(Opposite) This is a 5.28 kg (11.6 lb.) fragment from the largest aquamarine crystal ever found. The hexagonal prism, weighing 110.5 kg (243 lb.) and measuring 48.3 by 40.6 cm (19 by 16 in.), was discovered near Marambaia, Brazil, in 1910 and was so clear that, looking down the long axis, one could read a newspaper through it. The gemstone was cut in Idar-Oberstein, Germany, and yielded about 200,000 cts. of gems. A 47.39 ct. stone from Siberia, USSR, is shown for scale.

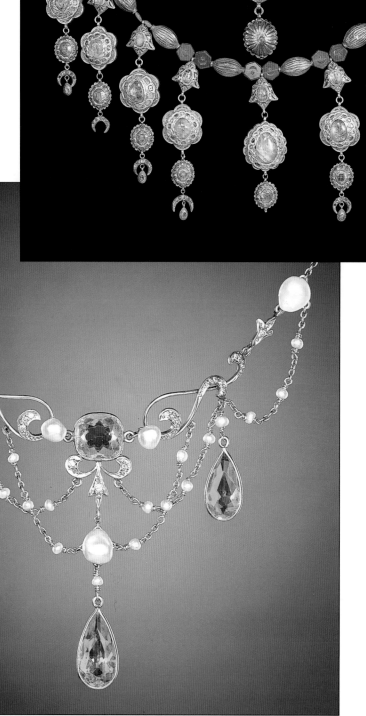

(Right) The official trapping of a vizier of Morocco (c. 1750). Aquamarines set in gold and surrounded by small diamonds, rubies, sapphires, and red garnets.

(Below) A delicate aquamarine necklace with pearls and diamonds dates from the early twentieth century.

(Opposite) Aquamarine brooch, earrings, and ring in platinum with diamonds. The simple, clean lines and the bold design of the swirl brooch are typical of the Art Deco style that developed during the 1930s. The large emerald-cut stone weighs 41.25 cts.

Legends and Lore

To the Romans, emerald symbolized the reproductive forces of nature and was dedicated to Venus; to the early Christians, it represented resurrection. In the fourth century B.C., Theophrastus noted its power to rest and relieve the eyes. Far later, Anselmus de Boot (1609) recommended emerald as the most powerful amulet to prevent epilepsy, stop bleeding, cure dysentery and fever, and avert panic.

In addition, an emerald was thought to give its owner the ability to foretell the future. According to Marbode, writing in the eleventh century, emerald improves memory, makes its owner eloquent and persuasive, and brings him joy. On the other hand, emerald was considered an enemy of sexual passion, and, in the thirteenth century, Albertus Magnus wrote that when King Bela of Hungary embraced his wife, his magnificent emerald broke into three pieces.

Aquamarine derives from two Latin words meaning "water" and "sea." Aquamarine amulets were thought to render sailors fearless and protect them from adversities at sea, especially if the stone were engraved with Poseidon on a chariot. The stone was a symbol of happiness and eternal youth, and according to Christian symbolism, it signified moderation and control of the passions to its owners. In medieval Europe, heliodor was believed to cure laziness.

An aquamarine cat's eye weighing 145 cts.,
from Minas Gerais, Brazil.

Occurrences

EMERALDS ARE MOST FREQUENTLY FOUND IN META-morphosed shales, particularly mica schists—the reason for some emeralds containing mica inclusions. In Colombia, emerald occurs in calcite veins in black shale (Muzo) and in quartz veins in limestone (Chivor). Aquamarine, morganite, and heliodor are found as well-formed crystals in pegmatites. Beryls are not sufficiently dense to concentrate in placers and are normally mined from the primary source or its weathered equivalent.

Colombia is the world's largest emerald producer with about 100 mines in operation. Muzo and Chivor are the two principal mines. Muzo yields the world's finest emeralds. Mining operations have continued there since the Spanish Conquest almost without interruption. In general, Chivor emeralds are less flawed but do not have as velvety an appearance as those from Muzo.

Mining of emeralds in Russia began shortly after a gem crystal was discovered in 1830 by a peasant in the Ural Mountains northwest of Ekaterinburg (Sverdlovsk). He took his find to the lapidary factory in Ekaterinburg, where geologist Jakov I. Kakovin recognized it as an emerald. Some years later, Kakovin's office was searched, and a large emerald crystal was found. Kakovin

was sent to prison, where he committed suicide. The 2226-gram crystal now resides in the Mineralogical Museum of the Academy of Sciences in Moscow. The Russian emeralds vary from fine deep green (but heavily included and flawed) to yellowish green (and less included).

Zambia emerged as a source of emerald in 1977. Emerald is also found in North Carolina. The best-known locality is around Hiddenite, where emeralds were discovered in 1880. Other occurrences are in Brazil and Pakistan.

Brazil is the principal source of aquamarine. More than 80 percent of the country's aquamarine comes from an area around Teofilo Otoni in the western part of Minas Gerais. The Malagasy Republic is known for the rich blue color of its aquamarine, which resembles sapphire. Aquamarine is also found in the Soviet Union in the Ural Mountains, in Transbaikalia, and in Siberia. Other occurrences of aquamarine include China, Pakistan, Afghanistan, and Maine, Idaho, and California.

The major sources of morganite are San Diego County in California, Minas Gerais in Brazil, and the Malagasy Republic. Heliodor is found in Minas Gerais and Goias, Brazil; the Ukraine in the Soviet Union; and also in Connecticut and Maine.

The Schettler Emerald weighs 87.62 cts., and its longest dimension is 3.5 cm (1 3/8 in.). It is engraved on both sides in a flower-and-leaf pattern and is probably from Muzo, Colombia.

An etched aquamarine crystal 8 cm (3 1/8 in.) tall, associated with white albite, from the Dusso area in Pakistan.

Evaluation

EMERALDS WITH A RICH, VELVETY GREEN UNIFORM color and a minimum of flaws are considered the finest quality. Skillful cutting can both minimize the visibility of inclusions and bring out the gem's best color. Emerald is often oiled to conceal cracks, and sometimes dye is added to improve the color—a fraudulent practice. Synthetic emeralds have been produced since 1934. Their prices are higher than those of other synthetics and even some natural emeralds.

Intensity of color and clarity are the most essential considerations in evaluating aquamarine, morganite, and heliodor. Aquamarine should be bright sky blue or sapphire blue. Aquamarines with intense color are becoming very scarce, and their price has increased substantially. The bright sky blue shade is now produced by heat-treating greenish yellow, greenish, and even brownish beryls. The color change is permanent. Gem-quality aquamarine is generally free from inclusions. Morganite should be deep purple pink, but peach colored gems are next best. Heliodor with a deep yellow to yellow green color is desirable.

A superb 58.79-ct. morganite from the Malagasy Republic.

GEMSTONES CONFUSED WITH GEM BERYLS

Emerald:	*Demantoid and tsavorite garnets, Imperial jade, tourmaline, peridot, green zircon, and hiddenite*
Aquamarine:	*Blue topaz, euclase, kyanite, apatite, sapphire, tourmaline, and zircon*
Morganite:	*Kunzite, tourmaline, topaz, sapphire, spinel, and rhodolite garnet*

Chrysoberyl & Spinel

CHRYSOBERYL

Alexandrite and cat's eye are renowned for their eye-catching properties, but few people know that they are varieties of a mineral that is more common in its transparent yellow green gemstone form. All three are chrysoberyl. Cat's eye chrysoberyl is *the* cat's eye; when spotlighted, the gem exhibits a band of light that opens and closes as the stone is turned. Alexandrite changes from red in incandescent light to green in daylight. It is *the* color-change gemstone. By comparison, ordinary chrysoberyl, though fine in its own right, seems a "poor relation."

An 85.0-ct. cat's eye from an unknown locality.

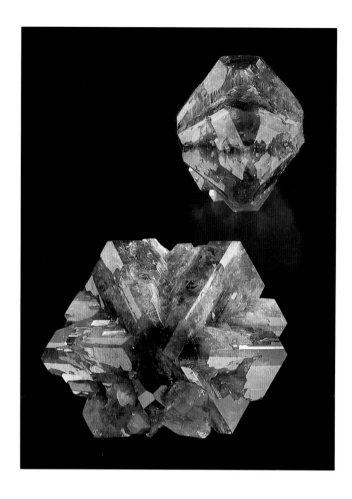

A chrysoberyl trilling, consisting of three twinned crystals, from Espirito Santo, Brazil; it measures 8 cm (3 1/8 in.) across—front and side view.

Properties

CHRYSOBERYL IS AMONG THE MOST BRILLIANT GEM-stones and only surpassed in hardness by diamond and corundum. The common variety is transparent yellowish green to greenish yellow and pale brown, the result of small amounts of iron replacing aluminum. Chromium is the coloring agent in green chrysoberyl and alexandrite. Alexandrite's pleochroism, which is the same as its color-change, is evident when the gemstone is viewed from perpendicular directions. The cat's eye is caused by fine needle inclusions of rutile (TiO_2) in one direction. Yellow, brownish, and green cat's eye are most common; alexandrite cat's eye is very rare.

Individual chrysoberyl crystals as rectangular prisms are rare. Instead, intergrowths (twins) called "trillings" or "sixlings" with near-hexagonal symmetry are more abundant.

CHRYSOBERYL DATA

Beryllium aluminum oxide:	$BeAl_2O_4$
Crystal symmetry:	Orthorhombic, pseudohexagonal
Cleavage:	Distinct in one direction
Hardness:	8.5
Specific gravity:	3.68-3.78
R.I.:	1.74-1.76 (moderate)
Dispersion:	Moderate

Historic Notes

THE TERM *CHRYSOBERYL* DERIVES FROM THE GREEK *chrysos*, referring to the stone's golden color, and the mineral beryl. Until 1789, when A.G. Werner, a famous German geologist, identified chrysoberyl as a mineral species, the stone was erroneously assumed to be a variety of beryl.

Cat's eye has the longest history of the chrysoberyl varieties. Although known in Rome by the end of the first century, it had been treasured even earlier in the Orient, where chatoyant stones have always had admirers. The gem was forgotten in the West until the late nineteenth century, when the Duke of Connaught gave a cat's eye betrothal ring to Princess Louise Margaret of Prussia. The gem's popularity—and price—rose immediately; Ceylon (Sri Lanka) had difficulty in keeping up with the demand. Cat's eye is currently a fashionable ring stone, particularly in Japan and Hong Kong.

Alexandrite was discovered in 1830 in an emerald mine near Ekaterinburg (Sverdlovsk) in the Russisan Ural Mountains on the birthday of the then heir apparent Czar Alexander II, for whom the gem was named. The naming was doubly appropriate not only because of the discovery date but because the chameleonlike green and red colors were the same as those of the Russian Imperial Guard.

The third and common variety of chrysoberyl, the transparent greenish yellow form, was found in Sri Lanka and Brazil. The Brazilians called it "crisolita" and named a city in its honor. Exported to Europe, the gem became popular and was used in eighteenth- and nineteenth-century Spanish and Portuguese jewelry. This variety of chrysoberyl was in great demand during the Victorian and Edwardian eras but is now overshadowed by alexandrite and cat's eye.

Chrysoberyls from Sri Lanka and Brazil, ranging in weight from 8.9 to 74.44 cts.

Legends and Lore

THE NATIVES OF SRI LANKA BELIEVED THAT CAT'S EYE PROtected its wearer from evil spirits. According to Hindu lore, it preserved an owner's health and guarded him or her against poverty. An Oriental belief was that, if pressed against the forehead at a point between the eyes, the gem would endow foresight.

Alexandrite has been regarded as a stone of good omen in Russia and is the only gem accorded the role of a talisman as recently as the nineteenth century.

An 8.9-ct. alexandrite from Sri Lanka, showing its color change—in incandescent light (red) and in daylight (green).

GEMSTONES CONFUSED WITH CHRYSOBERYL GEMS, SYNTHETICS, AND IMITATIONS

Alexandrite: *Synthetic sapphire and synthetic spinel are widely used as (usually poor) imitations. Synthetic alexandrite has had only marginal market success in the United States.*

Cat's eye: *Quartz and occasionally fine tourmaline cat's eye are commonly confused with chrysoberyl cat's eye. The unmodified name "cat's eye" applies only to chrysoberyl. Imitation cat's eye can be made by cutting synthetic or natural star sapphire in such a way as to display only one ray of the star. Cat's eye may also be imitated with triplets of white fibrous mineral ulexite sandwiched between two pieces of yellow synthetic sapphire or glass.*

Occurrences

CHRYSOBERYL CRYSTALLIZES IN AND AROUND pegmatites rich in beryllium, but deposits commonly form as alluvial concentrations from weathered pegmatites.

The major source of all chrysoberyl varieties is Minas Gerais in Brazil. Here, at Lavra de Hematita in 1987, the world's largest find of alexandrite produced, in less than three months, 50 kilograms of fine gems—some up to 30 carats. The Soviet Union alexandrite deposits near Sverdlovsk and one discovered later near the Sanarka River in the southern Urals are now apparently exhausted. Sri Lanka produces cat's eye and alexandrite from its gem gravels. Generally, the alexandrites are larger than the Russian stones and have more attractive daytime green color. However, the Russian alexandrite has a better color change and a finer red color under artifical light. Other occurrences of alexandrite are in Zimbabwe, Tanzania, and Burma.

Evaluation

ONLY CHRYSOBERYL WITH A DISTINCT COLOR CHANGE is alexandrite; either the red or green must be a good hue. Flaws diminish the value. Fine-quality stones exceeding 5 carats are both rare and expensive. Alexandrite cat's eye is one of the rarest and most costly of gems.

Cat's eye is the most valuable chatoyant gemstone. A rich honey yellow brings the highest price; the green stones follow in value. The chatoyant band must be sharp, narrow, and positioned in the center of the cabochon. In the finest stones, when the band is at right angles to the light, the half of the stone facing the light should appear milky; the other half should have a rich honey color. The eye should also open widely in oblique illumination and close sharply in direct illumination. Stones that approach transparency and exhibit a sharp eye command the highest price. Fine stones over 20 carats are rare and expensive. Of the common transparent variety of chrysoberyl, intensely colored yellowish green stones are the most popular and highly valued.

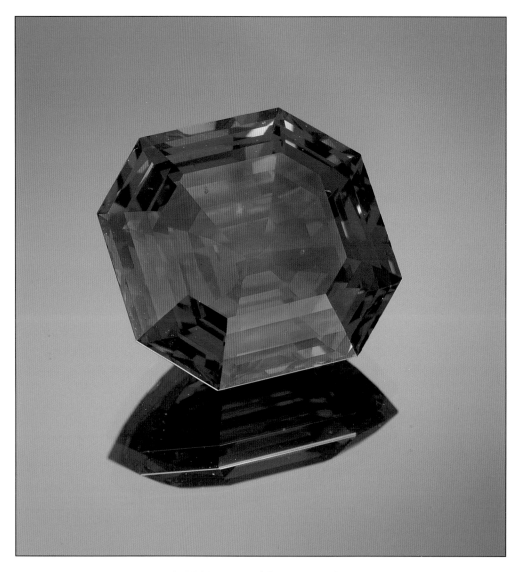

A 70.99-ct. spinel from Sri Lanka.

SPINEL

For centuries, most gem spinels were thought to be rubies or sapphires—a reasonable assumption, because both spinel and corundum are found in the same deposits and have similar properties. A famous example is the Black Prince's Ruby. The stone's known history began in 1367, when it was taken from the treasury of the King of Grenada by victorious Dom Pedro of Castile. He presented the "ruby" to the Black Prince, son of Edward III, in repayment for services at the Battle of Nájera in northern Spain. As part of the break-up of the crown jewels by the Commonwealth in the 1650s, the gem was sold (inventoried at four pounds Sterling) and somehow returned to the monarchy during the Restoration. The two-inch irregular spinel resides at the center of the British Imperial Crown.

Properties

LIKE THE CORUNDUM GEMSTONES WITH WHICH IT IS confused, spinel is known for its many colors and durability. Spinel is slightly softer than corundum because the magnesium to oxygen bonds in spinel are not quite as strong as the aluminum to oxygen bonds found in both minerals. This hardness, combined with no weak plane in its crystal structure, makes the gemstone very durable.

In another comparison to corundum, the presence of magnesium in addition to aluminum in spinel permits a wider range of chemical substitutions, transforming the pure colorless spinel into many possible colors but, surprisingly, not as many colors as corundum. Names have been applied to many of the different varieties, but now they are simply referred to by their color—red spinel, green spinel, etc. Synthetic spinels can be produced in an even greater range of colors by adding elements such as cobalt, manganese, and vanadium in amounts or combinations not found in nature.

Infrequently, spinels contain fine needles in three perpendicular directions that manifest four- and six-rayed stars in cabochon stones.

With cubic symmetry, spinel crystals are predominantly in the form of an octahedron. The term *spinel* may refer to this shape; the Latin *spina* means "thorn." Although spinels have probably been recognized by their octahedral crystals for many centuries, the distinction between ruby and spinel as different mineral species was not made until 1783 by Romé de Lisle.

Historic Notes

THE EARLIEST RED SPINEL USED AS AN ORNAMENT WAS found in a Buddhist tomb near Kabul, Afghanistan, and dates from about 100 B.C. Red spinel was also used by the Romans of the first century B.C. Blue spinels have been found in England dating from the Roman period (51 B.C.-A.D. 400), and a ring set with a pale green octahedral spinel from the Eastern Roman Empire has been described.

SPINEL DATA

Magnesium aluminum oxide:	$MgAl_2O_4$
Crystal symmetry:	Cubic
Cleavage:	None
Hardness:	8
Specific gravity:	3.58-4.06
R.I.:	1.714-1.75 (moderate)
Dispersion:	Moderate

Spinel is also the name of a mineral group of multiple oxides with the same crystal structure. **Gahnite,** *with zinc replacing magnesium, is a blue spinel gemstone.*

Mining of spinel began in Badakshan, Afghanistan, sometime between A.D. 750 and 950. The locality was first described by the Arab geographer Istakhri in 951 and later by Marco Polo. Many of the historic spinels (Balas rubies) were probably mined here.

Of the spinels, the red stones have had the longest and most dramatic histories. Like the Black Prince's Ruby, the Timur Ruby's known history goes back to the fourteenth century. The stone bears six Persian inscriptions, the oldest identifying it as being in the possession of the Tartar conqueror Timur (Tamerlane) in 1398. Over the years, the stone was traded or plundered in India until the East India Company took possession in 1849 and presented it to Queen Victoria two years later. The stone is now in the private collection of Queen Elizabeth II.

Red spinels were used in Renaissance jewelry in Europe and became popular during the eighteenth century. Elegant pendants, earrings, and brooches set with spinels and diamonds survive from the former Russian and French crown jewels. In Moscow, a deep red 412.25-carat spinel surmounts the Great Imperial Crown commissioned for the coronation of Catherine the Great. The world's largest collection of spinels, including a record-holding 500-carat stone, is part of the former crown jewels of Iran.

Legends and Lore

THE HINDUS CONSIDERED SPINELS TO BE RUBIES AND divided them according to caste. The members of each of the four major castes should wear the appropriate stone in order to benefit from its virtues: The Brahmin priestly caste—true ruby; Kshatriya (knights and warriors)—rubicelle; Vaisya (landowners and merchants)—ruby spinel; Sudra (laborers and artisans)—Balas ruby.

In ancient and medieval times, when color had strong symbolism, red spinel and other red stones were considered cures for hemorrhages and all inflammatory diseases—as well as prescriptions to soothe inflamed emotions, eliminating anger and conflict. An Indian belief, reported by an Armenian writer of the seventeenth century, is that powdered spinel taken in a potion eliminates dark forebodings and brings happiness.

Occurrences

GEM SPINELS, LIKE CORUNDUM, FORM IN HIGHLY METAmorphosed claystones and especially dirty limestones transformed into marbles. Most spinels are produced from alluvial concentrations from weathered primary sources.

The area around Mogok in Upper Burma is the source of the finest-quality spinels—rose, pink, orange, blue, and violet colors—which occur as water-worn pebbles and some as perfect octahedra. Sri Lanka's gem gravels are located in the southwest part of the island around Ratnapura ("City of Gems"). There the spinels, always water-worn, are generally blue, violet, or black (named "ceylonite" after the country's former name). Red, orange, and pink spinels are rare. Other occurrences are in Thailand, Pakistan, Afghanistan, and the Pamir Mountains of the Soviet Union.

GEMSTONE SPINEL COLORS, SOURCES OF COLORS, AND FORMER NAMES

Red: *Chromium (deep red—ruby spinel; rose red—Balas ruby)*
Purple red: *Chromium + iron (almandine spinel)*
Orange: *Chromium + vanadium (rubicelle)*
Blue: *Iron and/or cobalt (sapphire spinel and gahnospinel)*
Green: *Iron (chlorspinel)*

E*valuation*

Color, clarity, and weight are important considerations in appraising spinel. Red spinels are the most valuable, the most highly prized ones being orange red and intense red to purplish red. Because spinel is often flawless, its clarity is of great importance—much more important for spinel than for ruby, which is rarely found without inclusions. Stones weighing more than 5 carats are uncommon—the large ancient stones are no longer found.

Spinel possesses both beauty and durability, but confusion with the cheap synthetic version and insufficient supply prevent it from enjoying the popularity that it merits.

(Opposite) A 4.03-ct. cut spinel and an octahedral crystal 1 cm (3/8 in.) across in marble. Both are from Mogok, Burma.

(Above) Ring with 9.5-ct. spinel from Mogok, Burma. Other spinels, from Sri Lanka, range from 1.89 to 46.48 cts.

GEMSTONES CONFUSED WITH SPINEL AND SYNTHETIC SPINEL

Spinel can be mistaken for ruby, sapphire, pyrope garnet, amethyst, and zircon. Synthetic spinel is manufactured in large quantities, is inexpensive, and is used to imitate ruby, sapphire, emerald, aquamarine, peridot, alexandrite, and diamond.

Topaz

Topaz is renowned for its capacity to form large gem-quality crystals. Pliny in the first century remarked: "Topazos of all precious stones is the largest. In this, it excels all others." While in Minas Gerais, Brazil, in 1938, Allan Caplan, a New York mineral dealer, noticed with some excitement exceptionally large topaz crystals for sale. Upon learning the news, many United States museums began competing to obtain the "giants." The Smithsonian picked a topaz weighing 156 pounds; then the Cranbrook Institute got a slightly smaller one. Harvard, followed by the American Museum, wanted one, but no more were available.

During his fourth trip to Brazil in 1940, Caplan learned of three prodigious specimens in transit to Rio de Janeiro. On the basis of photographs alone, he bought them and returned home to await the arrival of his prizes, which were revealed to weigh 596, 300, and 225 pounds!

Finally, after many months, the crates arrived. At the U.S. Customs Office, eagerly and anxiously, Caplan approached the largest crate and removed the top boards. To his horror, he saw a great broken surface staring up at him from the packing material! Bitterly disappointed, he had the crate resealed and all three specimens sent to the American Museum for evaluation. There a group assembled for the grand opening. The moment arrived. The crate, now turned top side down, was pried open, and the superbly terminated "top" of the great crystal came into view. All in attendance breathed a collective sigh of relief as they gazed at the largest fine topaz crystal in "captivity"—and ever since a proud possession of the Museum.

Imperial topaz crystal, 5.5 cm (2 1/8 in.) long from Ouro Preto, Minas Gerais, Brazil, and a 16.95-ct. cut stone from Sri Lanka.

Properties

TOPAZ IS REVERED FOR ITS COLOR, CLARITY, AND HARD-ness. Strong chemical bonding makes it relatively dense and the hardest silicate mineral. However, a weak plane in the crystal structure occupied by fluorine and hydroxyl is the source of one excellent cleavage. This cleavage is topaz's major failing as a gemstone and demands great care in cutting and handling.

A common misconception is that all topaz is yellow. In fact, pure topaz is colorless, and colors include blue, pale green, and the spectrum from yellow through the familiar sherry orange to pink and even the most rare red. Chromium substitutes for aluminum, producing red and some pink topaz, but most other colors are a result of minor atomic substitutions and defects in the crystal followed by radiation damage. Some of these colors are unstable and can fade; some browns fade totally in sunlight, and some sherry orange stones become pink upon heating. High-energy irradiation of colorless topaz followed by heat treatment at moderate temperature yields blue stones with stable color. Natural blue topaz appears to be created by an identical process, so there is no way to distinguish between natural and "created" blues. However, intense natural blue stones are not known, so it is a good bet that deep blue color in gem topaz is artificially produced.

Topaz crystals typically form prisms having a diamond-shaped cross-section and a pyramidal top; the cleavage cuts straight through the prism.

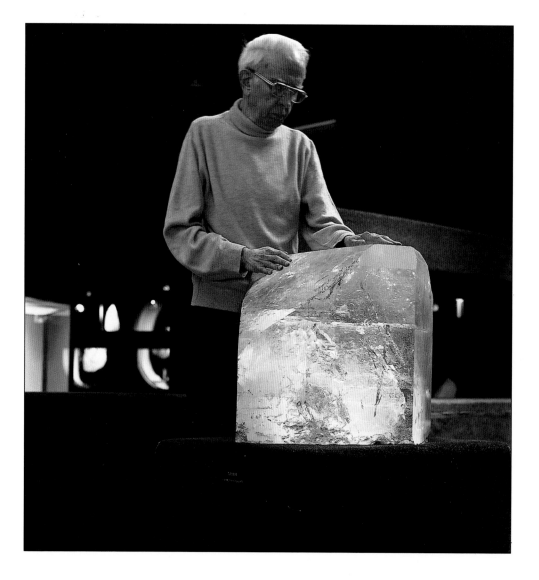

The world's largest topaz crystal, 271 kg (596 lb.), is from Minas Gerais, Brazil.

TOPAZ DATA

Aluminum silicate fluoride hydroxide:	$Al_2SiO_4(F,OH)_2$
Crystal symmetry:	**Orthorhombic**
Cleavage:	**Perfect in one direction**
Hardness:	**8**
Specific gravity:	**3.5-3.6**
R.I.:	**1.606-1.644 (moderate)**
Dispersion:	**Low**

Both the 47.55-ct. pink topaz and the 47.75-ct. Imperial topaz are from Minas Gerais in Brazil.

H*istoric* N*otes*

How topaz came by its name is uncertain. *Topazos,* which means "to seek," was the name of a fog-bound, hard-to-find island in the Red Sea (Zabargad). Pliny the Elder considered topazos to be a green stone from that island. However, since it is the green gemstone peridot—not topaz—that is found there, Pliny must have been describing peridot in this case. The Sanskrit *tapaz* means "fire" and seems a more appropriate possibility for the derivation of *topaz.*

Topaz was used in ancient Egypt and Rome; the Romans obtained their topaz from Ceylon (Sri Lanka), an early and continuing source for the gemstone. In the seventeenth century, Jean Baptiste Tavernier mentions both the stone and the location in accounts of his buying trips in the Orient.

During the Middle Ages in Europe, topaz was not particularly popular, although it was occasionally used in ecclesiastical or royal jewelry. But by the eighteenth century in Spain and France, the gem enjoyed increased popularity and, together with diamond, was set in many magnificent pieces of jewelry. Early in the next century, topaz and amethyst were the most stylish gems for earrings and necklaces in both France and England. Topaz continued to be one of the most popular gems during the Victorian era and later became a favorite stone of the Art Deco jewelers. Commonly regarded as the finest yellow stone, its popularity persists.

(Left) The largest faceted red topaz in the world is an oval brilliant-cut gem of 70.40 cts. with an unusual natural deep red color. It is either from Brazil or from the Soviet Union.

(Opposite) The Brazilian Princess was fashioned from a 34 kg (75 lb.) crystal discovered in Minas Gerais, Brazil. Cut in a square cushion form with 221 facets, it measures 14.5 cm (5 3/4 in.) across and weighs 21,005 cts. This gem is astounding both because of its size (the largest faceted blue topaz) and its nearly complete freedom from flaws.

Legends and Lore

DURING THE MIDDLE AGES, TOPAZ WAS THOUGHT TO strengthen the mind and prevent mental disorders as well as sudden death. Marbode's eleventh-century poetic treatise recommends it as a cure for weak vision. The prescription called for immersing the gem in wine for three days and three nights, followed by application of the topaz to the afflicted eye. A topaz engraved with the figure of a falcon could help its bearer cultivate the goodwill of kings, princes, and magnates, according to Ragiel's thirteenth-century *The Book of Wings*. Still later, topaz was recommended by Geronimo Cardano as a cure for madness, a means of increasing one's wisdom and prudence, and a coolant for both boiling water and excessive anger.

Occurrences

TOPAZ IS FOUND PRINCIPALLY IN GEM PEGMATITES, where fluorine is often abundant. This volatile-rich environment stimulates the growth of large crystals. Weathering of these pegmatites releases topazes into streams and rivers; the gemstones concentrate in alluvial gravels.

Minas Gerais in Brazil is the world's largest producer of topaz—blue, colorless, and sherry-colored. Topaz was discovered there first near Ouro Prêto in 1735, the primary source of sherry-colored topaz. In the Soviet Union's Ural Mountains, topaz is found northeast of Sverdlovsk in Mursinka and Alabashka and at Sanarka in the southern Urals. Another important Soviet site is Volini in the Ukraine. Topaz is mined north of Katlang in Pakistan in veins of coarse-grained calcite and quartz in marble that yield topaz of many colors, including a rare pink and reddish brown.

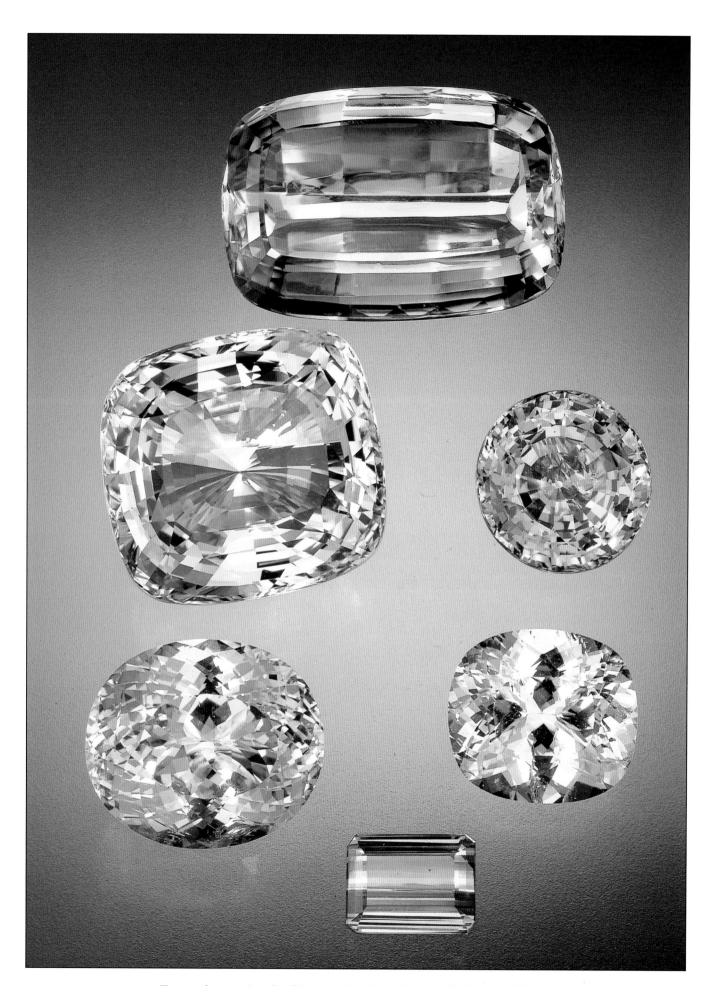

Topazes from various localities, ranging in weight from 17.16 cts to 375 cts.

Evaluation

TWO FACTORS SHOULD BE CONSIDERED IN EVALUATING topaz: color and clarity. The most valued color is a rare, almost unavailable, red. Imperial topaz, a sherry-colored stone, has always been the most popular. Both sherry-colored (brownish yellow, orangy yellow, and reddish brown) and pink topaz command high prices. Precious topaz is yellow topaz, a term commonly used to distinguish it from other topaz colors and from citrine. Light blue and pale yellow stones are of less value. The value diminishes significantly when the stone is flawed.

GEMSTONES CONFUSED WITH TOPAZ AND TRADE NAMES

Tourmaline, sapphire, chrysoberyl, and the rare danburite, andalusite, and apatite can be confused with topaz. Yellow quartz, or citrine, which lacks topaz's velvety appearance, brilliance, and rich color, is occasionally sold as topaz—an unethical practice. Equally unethical is the substitution of "treated" blue topaz for the rarer and more expensive aquamarine.

Misleading trade names are frequently used in substituting other less valuable stones for precious topaz: they include Spanish, Saxon, and Bohemian topaz for citrine quartz; Smoky, Burnt, and Scotch topaz for smoky quartz; and Oriental topaz for yellow sapphire.

Tourmaline

One spring morning in 1876, a young man walked briskly and confidently into Tiffany & Co. In the director's office, he unfolded a gem paper and placed what he later called a "drop of green light" on the desk. The "light" was a sparkling faceted green tourmaline from Maine, which spoke for itself. Both men admired its quality and beauty. Charles Tiffany bought it immediately, much to the delight of George F. Kunz. Within a year, the twenty-year-old gemologist had embarked on his illustrious career at the company. As the preeminent gem expert of his day, he championed lesser-known colored stones. Tourmalines were his favorites among American stones, and the timing of his visit was opportune. Several United States sites yielding commercially viable quantities of gem tourmaline had just been or were about to be discovered. Kunz collected tourmaline for many institutions, including the Museum—his Maine, Connecticut, and California tourmalines abound in the collections.

Bicolored tourmalines from Mesa Grande in California: three superb "pencil" crystals. The longest is 9.5 cm (3 3/4 in.). The cabochon is 22.40 cts., and the cut stone is 30.50 cts.

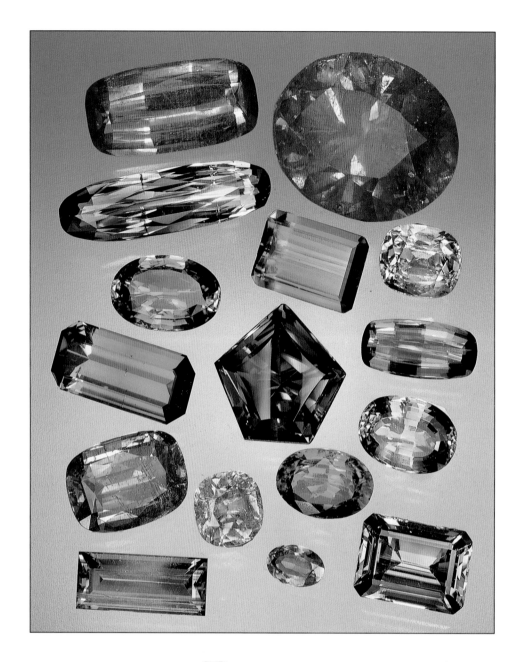

Properties

TOURMALINE IS A MINERAL GROUP WHOSE MEMBERS display the broadest spectrum of gemstone colors. There are ten mineral species in the group, but only three have found use as gems. These are sufficiently durable (hard and free from cleavage) to be fine gemstones. Named for the Isle of Elba, where it was first found, elbaite is the tourmaline most often used in jewelry; dravite and uvite are less common and rarely of the appropriate quality but are also gemstones. Gem elbaite can be pink to red, blue, green, violet to red purple, yellow, orange, brown, black, and colorless. Bicol-

ored crystals with one end green and the other pink are common. Crystals with a pink core and green rind are called "watermelon."

Color in gem tourmaline is primarily a result of substitutions of transition elements for other metals in the crystal structure. There are few useful generalities relating color to a specific chemical element, but pink is usually due to manganese, and green is attributed to ferrous iron, chromium, or vanadium. Color may be improved by heating and/or irradiation, but the changes are not always permanent.

TOURMALINE DATA

Complex aluminous borosilicates

Elbaite:	$Na(Li,Al)_3Al_6(BO_3)_3Si_6O_{18}(OH,F)_4$
Dravite:	$NaMg_3Al_6(BO)_3Si_6O_{18}(OH)_4$
Uvite:	$(Ca,Na)(Mg,Fe^{2+})Al_5Mg(BO_3)_3Si_6O_{18}(OH,F)_4$
Crystal symmetry:	*Trigonal*
Cleavage:	*None*
Hardness:	*7-7.5*
Specific gravity:	*3.03-3.25*
R.I.:	*1.610-1.675 (moderate)*

(Opposite) Faceted elbaites in different colors ranging in weight from 127.7 cts. to 1.270 cts., from various localities.

(Right) A superb bicolored elbaite crystal group 10.5 cm (4 1/8 in.) high from Tourmaline Queen Mine in Pala, California.

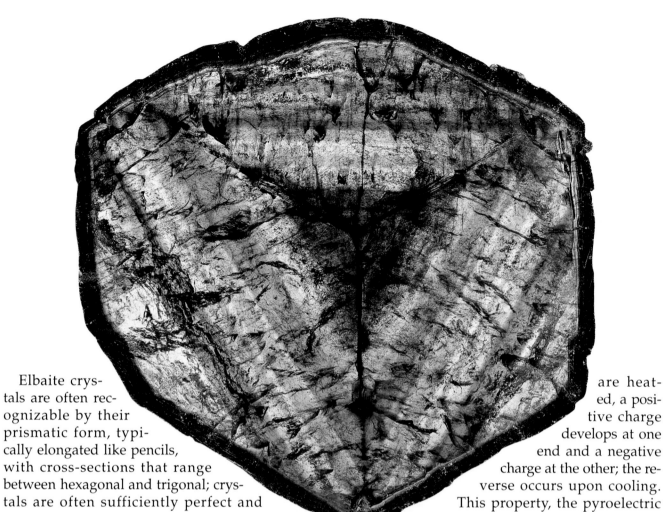

Elbaite crystals are often recognizable by their prismatic form, typically elongated like pencils, with cross-sections that range between hexagonal and trigonal; crystals are often sufficiently perfect and clear to be natural gems. Color zoning is created by changes in chemical composition in response to changing conditions during crystal growth. Elbaite crystals grow fastest at their ends, changing color as they grow and forming pencil-like bicolor crystals; layers of growth from core to rim produce the watermelons. Elbaite is the principal gem mineral that can be and is cut into bicolored and multicolored stones.

Most tourmalines are strongly pleochroic, an important factor in cutting gems; when viewed along the prism axis, the color is deeper or even different from that seen through the side of the crystal. Rare alexandrite-like tourmalines appear yellowish or brownish green in daylight and orange red in incandescent light. Crystals occasionally grow with fluid-filled tubes parallel to the long prismatic direction. If these are sufficiently numerous and narrow, like fibers, chatoyancy will be manifested from a properly fashioned gem.

The crystal structure of tourmaline lacks a center of symmetry; structural elements are much like arrows that point in one direction along the crystal's trigonal axis. As a result, when some crystals are heated, a positive charge develops at one end and a negative charge at the other; the reverse occurs upon cooling. This property, the pyroelectric effect, was first observed in gem tourmaline. A comparable electric charging is developed if pressure is applied to the ends of a crystal. This property, piezoelectricity, has important industrial and electronic applications. Among common gems, only tourmaline and quartz possess the properties of piezoelectricity and pyroelectricity.

SOME TOURMALINE VARIETIES AND COLORS

Rubellite: **Pink to red**

Siberite: **Violet to red purple**

Indicolite: **Blue**

Verdelite: **Green**

Achroite: **Colorless**

The new convention is simply to label tourmalines by their color, but old habits die hard.

H*istoric*N*otes*

A LONG-HELD BELIEF THAT TOURMALINE FROM THE Orient was imported by Greece and Rome was recently confirmed when a fine convex intaglio depicting the head of Alexander the Great (now in the Ashmolean Museum in England) was identified as a zoned purple yellow tourmaline. A minute inscription indicates India as the place of origin and the date of its carving as third or second century B.C. Another much later documented piece is a gold ring of Nordic origin from A.D. 1000 set with a pink tourmaline cabochon. Examination of surviving early jewelry will probably reveal more tourmalines, confirming that they have been used as a gem material for over 2,000 years.

The term *carbunculus* was applied to red transparent gems, including ruby, spinel, garnet, and probably red tourmaline from Pliny's time in the first century A.D. through the Middle Ages. Green tourmaline was exported from Brazil to Europe in

(Above) Bicolored elbaite from Brazil—carved rhinoceros, 85 cm (3 1/3 in.) long.

(Opposite) A polished slice of elbaite with liddicoatite rim, 13.2 cm (5 1/4 in.) wide, from the Malagasy Republic. Liddicoatite is a rare tourmaline species named in 1977 after gemologist R.T. Liddicoat.

Elbaite crystal measuring 20.5 cm (8 in.) with quartz crystal from Pala, California.

GEMSTONES FREQUENTLY CONFUSED WITH TOURMALINE

These include topaz, beryl (emerald, aquamarine, morganite, and golden beryl), spodumene (kunzite and hiddenite), peridot, andalusite, and apatite. Dark green synthetic spinel is sold as synthetic tourmaline.

the early sixteenth century; it was known as Brazilian emerald.

The Chinese valued red and pink tourmaline and made small carved tourmaline ornaments for headdresses and girdles, and certain mandarins wore badges or buttons on their caps to signify their rank. Gustavus III of Sweden chose an incredibly large "ruby" as a gift to Catherine the Great when he was on a state visit to Russia in 1777; it is, in fact, a stunning red Burmese tourmaline carved in China.

In 1703, a packet of stones from Sri Lanka labeled "turmali" or "toramalli" (a Sinhalese word applied to any unidentified yellow, green, or brown stone and meaning "something little out of the earth") arrived at a Dutch lapidary. According to one story, children playing with some of the "pebbles" outside a gem worker's shop noted that when warmed by the sun, the little stones attracted ashes and straws much as a magnet attracts iron filings. So the stones were called "Aschenstrekkers," or "ash-drawers." (As they are natural dust collectors, the Museum's tourmalines require frequent cleaning as a result of their daily heating by lights in the exhibit cases.) This discovery of tourmaline's pyroelectric property set off a spate of investigations resulting in observations that only certain gemstones, but with various colors, possessed this property. Finally in 1801, all the information came together with the recognition of the tourmaline "family."

During the eighteenth century, the principal sources of the mineral were Burma, Russia, Sri Lanka, and Brazil, but late one afternoon in 1820, two Maine schoolboys, Elijah L. Hamlin and Ezekiel Holmes, happened on a brilliant green crystal sparkling in the roots of an overturned tree as they returned from a hike on Mount Mica. The stone was identified as tourmaline, and, starting in 1822 with Mount Mica and later at other Maine locations, mines were opened that could provide sufficient red and green tourmaline to create a market—and value. With the Maine discoveries and several in California, the United States became for a time the world's major supplier of tourmaline. Among the purchasers was Tz'hsi (1835-1908), the dowager empress of China, who sent personal emissaries to California to purchase the favored red variety of the gem.

Legends and Lore

WITHOUT MANY CENTURIES OF ASSOCIATED HISTORY, the newcomer tourmaline gems do not appear in lore. Even George F. Kunz, popularizer of tourmaline and the man who introduced the stone to Tiffany & Co., opposed acceptance of the gem as the alternate birthstone for the month of October on that account. With the recent revival of mysticism, tourmaline has become a favorite of New Age adherents, who believe the mineral's pyroelectric and piezoelectric properties produce powerful amplification of psychic energy and neutralization of negative energies.

Occurrences

TOURMALINE IS A RELATIVELY COMMON MINERAL, THE most common boron-bearing silicate. Gem tourmaline is virtually restricted to pegmatites—rich in volatile elements like boron, beryllium, and lithium. Pegmatites yield not only crystals of elbaite but other gem minerals that contain these elements—gemstones such as spodumene and beryl.

Brazil is the world's major source of tourmaline. The pegmatitic region in the eastern part of Minas Gerais yields green, pink, red, and watermelon stones. Tourmaline is also produced in the states of Bahia, Ceara, Goias, Paraiba (blue), and Rio Grande de Norte. The United States also ranks high as a tourmaline supplier. The 400 pegmatitic dikes of Mesa Grande in San Diego County, California, produced 120 tons of gem tourmaline beween 1902 and 1911. Production reached its peak in 1910; however, with increased Brazilian supply and the fall of the last Chinese dynasty in 1912, California elbaite lost its markets, and many mines closed in 1914. Mining has been reactivated within the last 20 years. Most California elbaite is pink and pure in color, but it lacks the exceptional clarity of Maine elbaite. Pegmatites in eastern Maine, such as those at Newry, have been sporadically productive of the state's gem—tourmaline. Connecticut was a source at the beginning of the century. Other important sources include the Malagasy Republic, Sri Lanka (uvite), the Soviet Union, and Mozambique.

Tourmaline crystals from Mount Mica in Maine. The green tourmaline (upper left) is the original Maine find. Elijah Hamlin had it set in a watch charm bearing the inscription "Primus." It was given to the Museum by his great-granddaughter, K.B. Hamlin. The largest crystal is 5.3 cm (2 in.) long.

*Multicolored elbaite
crystal 7.3 cm (2 7/8 in.)
long, from Alto Ligohna,
Mozambique.*

(Right) A cluster of bicolored elbaite crystals 23.0 cm (9 in.) long from Nuristan, Afghanistan.

(Opposite) Pink elbaites from Pala, California—a crystal 10.0 cm (4 in.) long and a 419.5-ct. cut stone.

Evaluation

PURITY AND INTENSITY OF COLOR AND CLARITY ARE the most important qualities to consider. The most valued tourmalines are raspberry red, followed by medium-dark emerald green, and intense blue. Bicolored and multicolored gems are next in value. Cat's eye gems are valuable if the eye is well defined and the fibrous cavities causing it are not coarse.

During the past ten to fifteen years, tourmaline jewelry has been in great demand. Tourmaline crystals are also avidly sought by mineral collectors for the splendor of their colors and forms. George Kunz's faith in his "drop of green light" has been amply justified.

Zircon & Peridot

ZICON

In the 1920s, a new blue gemstone suddenly appeared on the market. Endowed with spectacular brilliance, it was an immediate hit. The gems were zircons, normally brown to green—but not blue. George F. Kunz, the legendary Tiffany gemologist, immediately suspected trickery; not only were these extraordinary stones available in abundance but available all over the world! Upon Kunz's behest, a colleague made inquiries during a trip to Siam (Thailand) and learned that a large deposit of unattractive brown zircon had stimulated color-improvement experimentation by local entrepreneurs. Heating in an oxygen-free environment had turned the drab material into "new" blue stones, which were sent to outlets worldwide. When the deception was revealed, the market simply accepted the information, and the demand for the new gems continued unabated.

Zircons from Sri Lanka and Thailand, ranging in weight from 7.76 to 40.19 cts.

Properties

SUPERIOR BRILLIANCE; GOOD DISPERSION, OR FIRE; clarity; and a breadth of colors stand out as zircon's fine gemstone qualities. Natural zircons range from colorless to pale yellow or green when they initially crystallize. The colors are a result of minor amounts of thorium and uranium that replace zirconium in the crystal structure. But with geologic time, uranium and thorium emissions cause radiation damage, which can be so severe that the original structure is obliterated. A glasslike substance develops with colors ranging from red to brown, orange, and yellow. Heat treatment can restore the structure and color or create new colors, including yellow, blue and colorless. Colorless zircons imitate diamond's optics better than any other gemstone mineral; their refractive indices approach diamond's, and the dispersive fire is nearly as good.

Many zircons are very brittle; a slight knock will remove a corner or even split the stone. This fragility is the result of internal stress either from radiation damage or from heat treatment. Zircon crystals are distinctive because of their square cross-section and pyramid terminations owing to the tetragonal symmetry.

ZIRCON DATA

Zirconium silicate: $ZrSiO_4$

Crystal symmetry: Tetragonal

Cleavage: None, but brittle

Hardness: 7.5

Specific gravity: 4.6-4.7

R.I.: 1.923-2.015 (high)

Dispersion: High

Note: Zircon is not cubic zirconia, a synthetic diamond simulant—zirconium oxide, ZrO_2.

Historic Notes

THE ARABIC ZAR AND GUN MEAN "GOLD" AND "color" and may be the source of the word we use. The terms hyacinth and jacinth were used in Europe for reddish brown and orange red stones and applied to zircons and other minerals with similar color.

The gem was in use in Greece and Italy as far back as the sixth century A.D. Gem zircons were marketed as diamonds some time after faceting began in the fourteenth century. Colorless zircon was mined at Puy en Velay in France in 1590 and sold as Diamond of France. Later, Ceylonese (Sri Lankan) colorless zircon was sold as Matura diamond (named for the locality where it was found).

Reddish brown zircon became moderately popular in Europe during the last century, but currently the most commonly used zircons are light blue, golden brown, and colorless.

Legends and Lore

ZIRCON IS AMONG THE GEMS UTILIZED IN THE KALPA Tree of Hindu religion. The tree was a symbolical offering to the gods and described by nineteenth-century Hindu poets as a glowing mass of precious stones, including sapphire, diamond, and topaz. Green zircon represented the tree's foliage.

As an amulet for travelers, zircon protected its wearer from disease and injury, ensured good sleep and a cordial welcome everywhere, according to the eleventh-century writings of Marbode. Five centuries later, the stone rendered its owner prudent in practical matters (and thus promised financial success) and guaranteed that he or she would never be struck by lightning, according to Geronimo Cardano. By the seventeenth century, the belief in magical properties of gems in general appeared to be waning. Anselmus de Boot declared that gems cannot of themselves produce supernatural effects. Nevertheless, he believed in zircon's power to prevent plague.

Occurrences

ZIRCON IS A COMMON MINOR CONSTITUENT OF igneous rocks, particularly granites, and, to a lesser extent, of metamorphic rocks. Gemstone crystals are rare and found mainly in coarse-grained rocks (pegmatites) or in fissures. Zircons concentrate in alluvial and beach deposits.

The Chanthaburi area in Thailand, the Palin area in Cambodia, and the southern part of Vietnam near the Cambodian border are the major sources of zircon. It occurs as water-worn pebbles in gem gravels which are seldom more than 10 feet deep. Bangkok is the world's cutting and marketing center for zircon. Blue, colorless, golden yellow, orange, and red stones, almost all of them heat-treated, are exported from there.

Sri Lanka, where zircon is also found in gem gravels, is the next most important source. Other occurrences are in Burma, France, Norway, Australia, and Canada.

Round brilliant-cut zircon from Thailand; weighing 208.65 cts., it is the largest known blue zircon on public display.

Evaluation

COLOR AND CLARITY ARE THE MOST IMPORTANT CONsiderations in evaluating zircon. The most prized and rare color is red; next is pure, intense blue and sky blue. Colorless, orange, brown, and yellow are less valued. Any visible flaw diminishes the value substantially.

Most zircons have been heat-treated. The color of some of the heat-treated stones may change, and the brittleness of some treated gems is also a negative factor. The beauty of this gem—expressed in the variety of its colors and in its clarity, brilliance, and fire—makes it popular today. It is also reasonably priced in comparison with most other gems.

PERIDOT

For three millennia, a small, desolate, and forbidding island in the Red Sea has been exploited for the gemstone. Nothing grows on this spot of land, there is no fresh water, and the brutal heat relents only in the middle of winter. From the port of Râs Banâs in Egypt, small boats are still used to cross the more than thirty miles of shark-infested water to reach the island. The beaches near the deposits are green with tiny gem crystals. March up Peridotite Hill through the ancient diggings, and you find the fissures lined with complete and fractured gem crystals measuring from millimeters to several centimeters. The island is Zabargad, Arabic for *olivine*—the gemstone peridot. For peridot, Zabargad has been the most important and illustrious source.

P*roperties*

OLIVE TO LIME GREEN COLOR IS THE MOST IMPORTANT quality for peridots. This characteristic color is caused by iron; the color saturation increases with iron content, but too much iron yields a brownish tinge. Most peridot is about 90 percent forsterite and the rest fayalite. The transparent gemstone has reasonably good properties: moderate durability and brilliance with a slightly greasy-looking luster.

Peridot crystal 4.1 cm (1 5/8 in.) long and a 10.92-ct. cut stone, both from Zabargad Island, Egypt.

PERIDOT DATA

A variety of forsterite, Mg_2SiO_4, which with fayalite, Fe_2SiO_4, constitutes a complete series (solid solution) in the olivine group of minerals.

Magnesium iron silicate:	*$(Mg,Fe)_2SiO_4$*
Crystal symmetry:	*Orthorhombic*
Cleavage:	*Imperfect in two directions*
Hardness:	*7*
Specific gravity:	*3.22-3.45*
R.I.:	*1.635-1.690 (moderate)*

A 164.16-ct. peridot from Burma (top); the other gems are 61.55 and 95.19 cts., both from Zabargad Island.

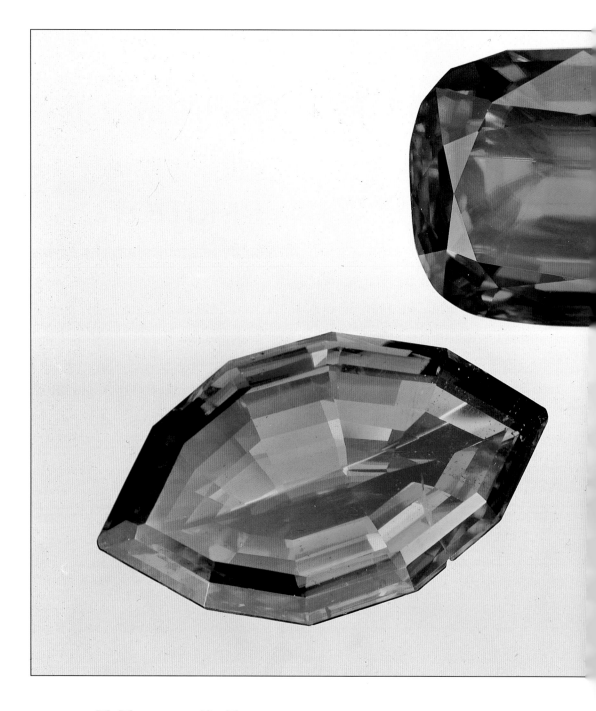

Historic Notes

THE EGYPTIANS FASHIONED PERIDOT BEADS AS EARLY as 1580-1350 B.C. Second- and first-century B.C. writings of the Greek geographers Agatharchides and Strabo described Zabargad and its mining operations. In the third and fourth centuries in Greece and Rome, the gemstone was used for intaglios, rings, inlays, and pendants.

During the Middle Ages, the Crusaders brought peridot back to Europe; some of these gems are preserved in European cathedrals. Peridot was highly prized late during the Ottoman Empire (1300-1918). Turkish sultans amassed the world's largest collection of them. In Istanbul's Topkapi Museum, there is a gold throne decorated with 955 peridot cabochons ranging up to an inch across, peridots in turban ornaments and on jeweled boxes, and literally thousands of loose peridots.

When the term *peridot* was first used is

Legends and Lore

FROM EARLY TIMES THROUGH THE MIDDLE AGES, peridot was considered a symbol of the sun. An early Greek manuscript on precious stones tells us that peridot bestows royal dignity on its wearer. Another belief was that the stone would protect its owner from evil spirits; in order to do so, the gem must be pierced, strung on the hair of an ass, then tied around the wearer's left arm, a procedure outlined by Marbode. A thirteenth-century English manuscript states that if a torchbearer, sign of the sun, is engraved on the gem, it will bring wealth to its owners.

Occurrences

FORSTERITE IS COMMON IN BASALTS AND PREDOMINANT in peridotite rock, but large unfractured peridot crystals are rare. At Zabargad, Egypt, the peridotite verges on being a pegmatite. Zabargad is presently inactive, awaiting better times in the Middle East.

The major source of peridot for the last fifteen years has been peridotite on the San Carlos Indian Reservation in Arizona. The stones are small, rarely exceeding 5 carats. The only source of large masses of fine-quality peridot is Upper Burma, near Mogok. Other occurrences are in Minas Gerais in Brazil, Sunnmore (formerly Söndmore) in Norway, China, and Kenya.

Evaluation

uncertain; French jewelers used it long before French mineralogist R.J. Haüy (1743-1822) applied it to the mineral. Yellow green peridot is sometimes called *chrysolite,* a term deriving from the Greek words meaning "gold" and "stone."

During the nineteenth century, the peridot became popular in both Europe and the United States, and production on Zabargad was active during the first half of this century.

THE GREENER THE PERIDOT, THE HIGHER ITS VALUE. A tinge of brown diminishes its price, and any flaws make the stone undesirable. Usually, the price per carat does not increase with size. Peridot may be confused with tourmaline, green zircon, green garnets, chrysoberyl, diopside, moldavite (a tektite—natural glass), and sinhalite.

Turquoise & Lapis Lazuli

TURQUOISE

Turquoise is a gemstone with two probable firsts—first to be mined and first to be imitated. Indirect evidence suggests that the Wadi Maghara and Serabit El Khadem mines on the Sinai Peninsula were in production before 3100 B.C. Egyptian turquoise beads dating to 4000 B.C. have been found at al Badari. Surviving records from the time of King Semerkhet (c. 2923-2915 B.C., during the First Dynasty) document extensive mining operations that employed thousands of laborers and continued until about 1000 B.C. By 3100 B.C., either supplies were not meeting demand or a cheaper substitute was desired, because imitations (soapstone glazed blue and green—a form of faïence) are found as artifacts of this period.

A 90.20-ct. cabochon of turquoise with spiderweb matrix from Santa Rita in New Mexico and a 93.98-ct. high cabochon from Iran.

Properties

COLOR IS TURQUOISE'S SUPERLATIVE GEM PROPERTY; the mineral's other properties are less than ideal. The gemstone usually forms in aggregates of submicroscopic crystals that make it opaque. Turquoise is relatively soft and subject to scratching. Its porosity makes it discolor by absorption of oils and pigments, and friability can lead to easy breakage; only the most compact varieties resist these tendencies. The sky blue color is intrinsic, a result of copper. Iron in turquoise leads to greener tones. Ochre or brown black veining is common, the result of oxide staining or inclusion of adjacent rock fragments during turquoise's formation.

The turquoise Chou Dog was carved in China from Tibetan material and is 6.1 cm (2 3/8 in.) long.

TURQUOISE DATA

Copper aluminum phosphate:	$CuAl_6(PO_4)_4(OH)_8 \cdot 5H_2O$
Crystal symmetry:	*Triclinic (normally cryptocrystalline)*
Cleavage:	*Not observed in massive gemstone form*
Hardness:	*5-6*
Specific gravity:	*2.6-2.8*
R.I.:	*1.62 average*

Bone scraper inlaid with turquoise and jet, 15 cm (6 in.) long, found during the 1896 Hyde Expedition in Pueblo Bonito, Chaco Cañon, New Mexico.

Historic Notes

THE NAME *TURQUOISE* DID NOT COME INTO USE UNTIL the thirteenth century. Pliny used the term *callais*, derived from the Greek *kalos lithos*, meaning "beautiful stone." Purchased by Venetian merchants in Turkish bazaars for European trade, the blue stone was called "pierre turquoise" by the French recipients, meaning "Turkish stone."

The first uses of turquoise were in Mesopotamia (Iraq), where beads dating from about 5000 B.C. have been found. Turquoise is Iran's national gemstone. It has decorated thrones, daggers, sword hilts, horse trappings, bowls, cups, and ornamental objects. High officials once wore turquoise seals decorated with pearls and rubies. Large stones were embellished with gold scrollwork to hide the imperfections. After the seventh century A.D., turquoise pieces decorated with

passages from the Koran or Persian proverbs in incised gilt characters were treasured as amulets. Turquoise has been the most cherished gem in Tibet as well, with a role comparable to that of jade in China.

Turquoise was frequently set in Siberian jewelry of the fifth and sixth centuries B.C. and in pieces from southern Russia of a slightly later date. The ancient Greeks and Romans engraved turquoise for ring stones and pendants and also used it as beads, but certainly it was not one of their favorite stones. In Europe, it became more popular during the Middle Ages for decoration of vessels and the covers of manuscripts. Popularity of the stone for personal adornment grew during the Renaissance; by the seventeenth century, "no man considered his hand well-adorned" unless

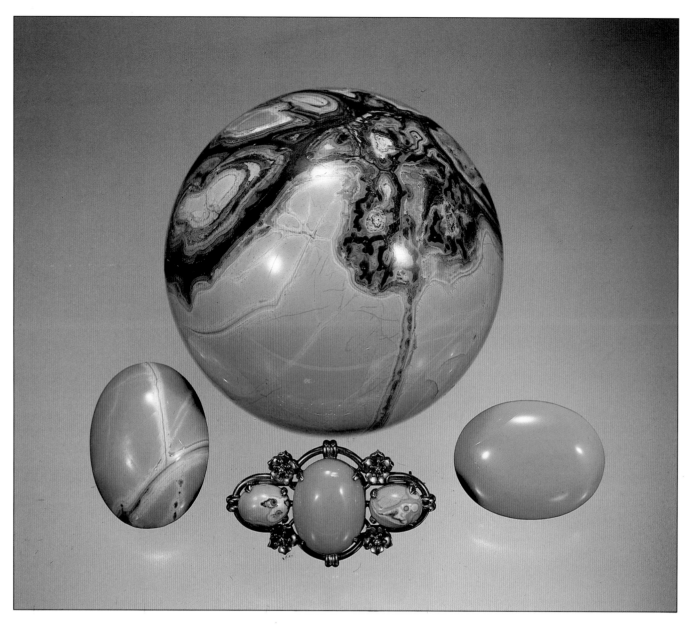

A polished variscite sphere 7.5 cm (2 15/16 in.) in diameter, two cabochons, and a gold pin with three cabochons from Fairfield, Utah. Variscite is often mistaken for turquoise.

he wore a turquoise, according to Anselmus de Boot. In the following centuries, turquoise remained popular, gracing royal crowns as well as modest jewels. In Europe, it has been the most popular opaque gemstone.

The gem's history in the Americas began about 1,000 years ago with the initiation of turquoise mining at Mount Chalchihuitl in Cerrillos, New Mexico. Native Americans, using hand tools, quarried the entire mountain; all that remains on the north side is a pit about 200 feet across and up to 130 feet deep.

Turquoise has been found in burial sites in Argentina, Bolivia, Chile, Peru, Mexico, Central America, and the southwestern United States. The Incas carved beads and figurines and crafted beautiful turquoise inlays. The Aztecs used turquoise in mosaic pendants and ritual masks. The Zuni, Hopi, Pueblo, and Navajo all made magnificent necklaces, ear pendants, and rings. At Pueblo Bonito in northwestern New Mexico, nearly 9,000 beads and pendants were found near a single skeleton. All told, 24,932 beads were found in these burial sites.

Legends and Lore

IN PERSIA (IRAN), ONE WHO COULD SEE THE REFLECtion of a new moon on a turquoise was certain to have good luck and be protected from evil. Hindus had a comparable belief: if an individual could look at a new moon and immediately after at a piece of turquoise, great wealth would surely follow. To the Navajos, a piece of turquoise thrown into a river (while a prayer to the rain god was being spoken) would ensure the blessing of rain. A turquoise attached to a gun or bow would guarantee accurate aim, according to Apache lore.

The belief that turquoise would protect its owner from falling—especially from a horse—is first recorded in the thirteenth century. The virtue traces to turquoise's use in Persia and Samarkand as a horse amulet. Legend also has it that, by changing color, turquoise reveals a wife's infidelity.

Occurrences

TURQUOISE CRYSTALLIZES AS VEINS AND NODULES near the water table in semiarid to arid environments. Its chemical stockpiles are the adjacent rocks, which are leached by rain and ground water; thus turquoise is often associated with weathered igneous rocks containing primary copper minerals.

Before World War I, turquoise production from nearly 100 mines was Iran's most important industry. Following World War II, output declined and ceased altogether with the revolution. Turquoise is found in Nevada, Arizona, Colorado, New Mexico, and California, the primary producers of turquoise today. Much of the turquoise is a byproduct of copper mining. Most American turquoise is light in color, porous, and chalky, usually with matrix, and only 10 percent of the turquoise mined is of gem quality. Other occurrences are in Armenia and Kazakhstan in the Soviet Union, China, Australia, Tibet, Chile, Mexico, and Brazil.

Evaluation

THE INTENSITY AND EVENNESS OF COLOR AND QUALIty of polish affect the value of turquoise. The very rare, intense sky blue (robin's egg blue) is most desired. Turquoise with matrix is generally less valuable than stones without it. Of matrix turquoise, the spiderweb variety is the most valuable.

A fine polish is possible only with stones that are hard, relatively nonporous, and compact. Very pale and chalky turquoise is sometimes impregnated with oil, paraffin, liquid plastic, glycerin, or sodium silicate to enhance its color and ability to take a good polish. Occasionally, this turquoise is sold as stabilized turquoise or turquolite. Some turquoise is even painted on the surface with blue dye and then coated with clear plastic. Much of the turquoise on the market has been treated in these ways, and some may change color.

GEMSTONES CONFUSED WITH TURQUOISE, IMITATIONS, AND SYNTHETICS

Chrysocolla, chrysocolla quartz, odontolite (a naturally stained fossilized bone), variscite, and malachite are easily confused with turquoise. Turquoise may be imitated with glass, porcelain, plastic, enamel, stained chalcedony, dyed howlite, blue-dyed and plastic-treated marble, and doublets. Artificial products are sold with names such as Viennese turquoise, Hamburger turquoise, and Neolith. Synthetic turquoise has been produced and marketed in France since 1970.

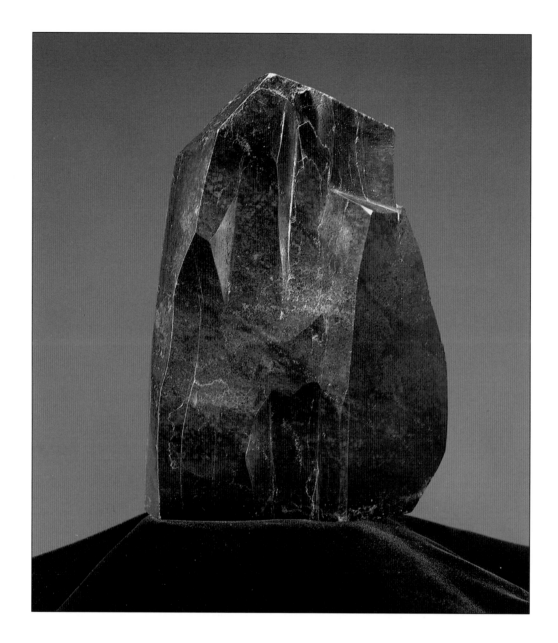

LAPIS LAZULI

Lapis lazuli is probably the original blue gemstone and has an ancient history of exploitation in Afghanistan. The gemstone has been so important to Afghanistan that lapis figured in United States foreign policy. In 1985, during Senate Armed Services Committee hearings on the war in Afghanistan, some testimony indicated that lapis lazuli was an important source of cash for the mujahadeen to buy weapons to battle the Soviet-backed regime. In fact, the Kabul government was also trying to raise cash by selling quantities of the blue stone. The result for the market has been an unusual abundance of lapis available in recent years. Unfortunately, although there may be tons to pick from, only a minute proportion has the fine and uniform blue color with only occasional golden flecks that distinguish the most desirable lapis lazuli.

LAPIS LAZULI DATA

A rock composed principally of the mineral lazurite [a sodium aluminosilicate containing sulfur, chlorine, and hydroxyl—$(Na,Ca)_{7-8}(Al,Si)_{12}O_{24}[(SO_4),Cl_2,(OH)_2]$ with variable amounts of pyrite (the brassy flecks) and white calcite

Cleavage:	*Not relevant for a rock*
Hardness:	*5-5.5*
Specific gravity:	*2.7-2.9*
R.I.:	*About 1.5 (opaque)*

(Opposite) Polished lapis lazuli boulder from Afghanistan, 13.5 cm (5 1/4 in.) high.

(Below) Lapis lazuli Chinese junk, 15.2 cm (6 in.) high.

Properties

AS LAPIS LAZULI IS OPAQUE, THE MOST IMPORTANT qualities are color and a moderate durability. Lazurite is not very hard, but fine-grained lapis is reasonably tough. The intrinsic blue color of lazurite is caused by sulfur, an interesting and unusual case where a nonmetallic element yields a strong color. Lapis was ground into the pigment ultramarine until an artificial replacement was developed in 1828.

Historic Notes

IN EGYPT, CARVED LAPIS BEADS, SCARABS, PENDANTS, and lapis-inlaid jewelry date prior to 3100 B.C. The stone was esteemed as a gem and amulet. Ground into powder, it was used as a medicine and a cosmetic—the first eye shadow.

The tomb of Queen Pu-abi (2500 B.C.) in the city of Ur in Sumer contained adornments rich with lapis—three gold headdresses, two bead necklaces, a gold choker, a silver pin, and a gold inlaid ring.

During the time of Confucius (c. 551-479 B.C.), the Chinese carved lapis hair and belt ornaments. As early as the fourth century B.C., the Greeks used lapis for carving scarabs and scaraboids, and it was described by Theophrastus. In Rome, lapis was fashioned into intaglios, plain ring stones, beads, and inlays. The ancient Greeks and Romans used the term *sapphirus*; *lapis lazuli* did not come into use until the Middle Ages. *Lazulus* means "blue stone" in Latin and derives from the ancient Persian *lazhuward*, meaning "blue," and the Arabic *lazaward*, meaning "heaven," "sky," or simply "blue in general."

The stone was a favorite material for carving *objets d'art* during the Renaissance in Europe. When Catherine the Great was told that lapis had been discovered near Lake Baikal, she ordered that mining be commenced immediately. In the following year, 1787, the empress decorated a room in her palace in Tzarskoye Selo (now Pushkin) with the stone. Sections of walls, doors, fireplaces, and even mirror frames were made of lapis.

Today, lapis is favored for beads, ring stones, and pendants and is a preferred stone for men's jewelry.

Legends and Lore

TO THE BUDDHISTS, LAPIS BROUGHT ITS OWNER peace of mind and equanimity and dispelled evil thoughts. In *De Materia Medica* (c. A.D. 55), Greek physician and pharmacologist Dioscorides recommended lapis as an antidote for the bite of a poisonous snake. By the thirteenth century, broadened curative powers were attributed to lapis; Albertus Magnus advised using lapis for intermittent fever and melancholy in his mineralogical treatise.

GEMSTONES CONFUSED WITH LAPIS LAZULI, SUBSTITUTES, AND IMITATIONS

Sodalite, azurite, lazulite, and dumortierite may be confused with lapis lazuli. The most common substitute for lapis is blue-dyed chalcedony, sold as German lapis and Swiss lapis. Lapis has been imitated with synthetic spinel with gold forced into surface holes to simulate inclusion of pyrite (fool's gold).

Occurrences

LAPIS IS A RARE METAMORPHIC ROCK PRODUCED BY the interaction of granitelike magma with marble. In addition to Afghanistan, Chile is a major source of the gemstone. The most productive mine is in the Andes in Coquimbo Province, north of Santiago. It was worked by the Incas in pre-Columbian times and continues in production today. A less important source is near Antofagasta. Chilean lapis usually contains large amounts of calcite, although mining of better-grade material has been reported recently. The Soviet Union produces the stone from mines near Lake Baikal and near Khorog in the Pamir Mountains. In the United States, lapis is produced in Colorado and in California.

Evaluation

THE QUALITY, PURITY, AND EVENNESS OF COLOR LARGEly determine the value of lapis. The most desired color is deep violet blue. Stones without inclusions of pyrite or calcite are most desirable. Lapis with inclusions of pyrite is more valuable than that with inclusions of calcite. Often the white calcite inclusions are disguised with paraffin treatment, which may include the use of blue dye. (Dye can be detected by rubbing the stone with cotton dipped in acetone or fingernail-polish remover; the blue color comes off on the cotton. In fact, this test works for most dyed gems.) The minerals in lapis have unequal hardnesses and polish differently. Only superior, inclusion-poor lapis can be polished to a smooth, even luster.

Russian lapis lazuli carving decorated with sterling silver, yellow gold, red and yellow enamel, and small rose-cut diamonds. It measures 16 cm (6 1/4 in.) across, and the base is stamped by the famous Fabergé workshop.

O*pal*

The sheer beauty of opal outweighs its disadvantageous physical properties. Rainbow colors pour out of well-lit precious opals, but the gems are easily scratched and so are a poor choice for exposed ring settings. Opals are mechanically fragile and notoriously difficult to set in jewelry; a slight blow or a rapid change in temperature may shatter an opal. The problem is that the gem contains water, which—depending on the opal and its source—may evaporate and leave the opal slightly smaller, stressed, and covered with cracks. Opals need our protection; worn close to the body, they are safe from abrasion, are kept at an even temperature, and receive some body moisture so that they do not lose water.

Opalized wood, 9 cm (3 1/2 in.) long, from Virgin Valley, Nevada.

Properties

THE CHARACTERISTIC FEATURE OF GEM OPAL IS PLAY of colors; pure colors can be seen in rapid succession when the gem is moved about. By some standards, opal is not a mineral because it does not have an extended crystal structure. Opal is made up of submicroscopic silica spheres bonded together with more silica and water. The lower the initial amount of water in the opal, the better are its properties. Loss of water or change in temperature causes strain that is relieved by cracking, known as crazing. Also, opal is soft, and its density and refractive index are low.

If the minute spheres in opal are uniform in size and packed into a regular array, they can scatter light in various colors (by diffraction) determined by the size of the spheres and the opal's orientation. Gem or precious opal contains many of these organized zones that display diffraction colors, whereas common opal may be colored but does not show a play of colors. Precious opal is usually cut as a cabochon or carved, but some fire opal is sufficiently transparent to be faceted.

Opals from Mexico ranging in weight from 4.72 to 31.70 cts.

OPAL DATA

Hydrated silica:	$SiO_2 \cdot nH_2O$
Crystal symmetry:	*Largely amorphous*
Cleavage:	*None, but brittle*
Hardness:	*5.5-6.5*
Specific gravity:	*1.98-2.25*
R.I.:	*1.43-1.47 (low)*
Special optical property:	*Diffraction—play of colors*

Pendant 4.5 cm (1 3/4 in.) in length, set with Australian opals, chrysoberyl, sapphires, topaz, demantoid garnets, and pearls.

PRECIOUS OPAL BODY COLORS AND THEIR CAUSES

PRECIOUS OPALS ARE GENERALLY DEFINED BY MANIFESTING A PLAY OF COLORS.

Black:	*A black or dark background in gray, blue, or green—dark inclusions*
White:	*A white background—internal boundaries or fluid inclusions*
Water:	*A transparent or colorless stone—few or no inclusions*
Fire:	*A transparent stone (play of color may or may not appear) or translucent yellow, orange, red, or brown—ochre-colored iron oxide in inclusions*

OPAL CLASSIFICATION BY SIZE AND PATTERN OF COLOR PATCHES

Pinpoint or pinfire:	*Small patches, close together*
Harlequin:	*Larger, more angular patches that resemble the diamonds of a harlequin pattern*
Flame:	*Red streaks and bands that cross the surface like flames*
Flash:	*Flashes of color that appear and disappear when the stone is moved*

Historic Notes

Opal derives from the Sanskrit *upala* and the Latin *opalus*, meaning "precious stone." Pliny described fine opals: "In the opal you will see the refulgent fire of the carbuncle, the glorious purple of amethyst, and the sea green of the emerald, and all these colors glittering together in incredible union."

The oldest opal mine was at Czerwenitza, now in Czechoslovakia (formerly Hungary). Archival evidence indicates that the mine was worked in the fourteenth century, but there are indications that it was in operation much earlier—perhaps the source of opal for Rome. Production of semitranslucent milky-white stones with play of color continued until 1932. Mexican fire opal was known to the Aztecs and was introduced in Europe by the Spanish conquistadors early in the sixteenth century.

Shakespeare referred to opal as "the queen of gems" in *Twelfth Night*. Opal's prominence declined during the nineteenth century, when the stone was associated with bad luck. Many believe that Sir Walter Scott was responsible. In his 1828 novel, *Anne of Geierstein*, the heroine's demonic grandmother died when a drop of holy water touched her enchanted opal and put out its fire.

Black opal was first found in Australia in 1887. Queen Victoria helped popularize it and white opal by giving opal jewelry to all of her children. Opal was a favorite stone of René Lalique (1860-1945), the most talented artist-jeweler of the Art Nouveau movement. He designed opal jewelry for Sarah Bernhardt (1844-1923) among others.

Black and white opals are currently among the most popular gems.

Legends and Lore

The Romans considered opal a stone of love and hope. The Arabs believed it fell from heaven in flashes of lightning. Marbode wrote of an opal talisman of the House of Normandy: "It renders the wearer invisible, enabling him to steal by day without risk of exposure to baneful dews of night." Thus the opal became known as the talisman of thieves and spies. Anselmus de Boot summarized: "Opal possesses the virtues of all gems as it displays their many colors."

According to an Australian legend, the stars are governed by a huge opal that also controls gold in the mines and guides human love. However, the Australian aborigines had a negative slant: opal is a devil, half-serpent, half-human, who lurks in a hole in the ground ready to lure men to destruction with flashes of wicked magic.

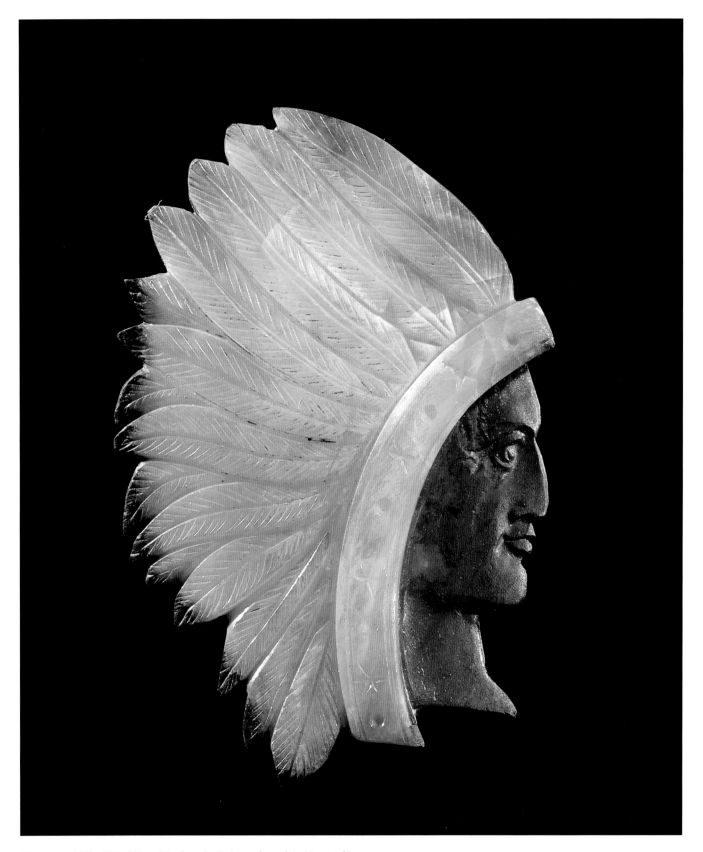

(Opposite) The 215.85-ct. Harlequin Prince, found in Australia.

(Above) Opal Indian head carving measuring 4.2 cm (1 4/5 in.) in length. The rough opal is from Myneside, West Queensland, Australia.

Occurrences

OPAL IS FORMED IN CAVITIES AND CRACKS IN NEAR-surface volcanic rocks or as replacements—thus making fossils—of shells, bones, and wood in or near sedimentary volcanic ash by percolating water that dissolves silica and then precipitates opal.

Australia produces 85 percent of the world's opal. Lightning Ridge, New South Wales, is the primary source of black opal. Coober Pedy, discovered in 1915, is the opal capital of the world. The aboriginal name for the location, Kupa Pita, means "white man in a hole." The miners and their families all used to live underground, attempting to escape the intolerable climate; some still do. (Thus the aboriginal legend is made a little clearer.) White Cliffs and Andamooka are also important sources.

The only commercial source of fire opal is Mexico, principally near Querétaro, where mining began in 1870. Mexican fire opal is softer and lighter than opal from other sources because it contains more water. The states of Jalisco, Hidalgo, Guanajuato, and Nayarit also produce opal.

Opal was discovered at Virgin Valley in Nevada in 1908. This material is very beautiful, but once it is exposed to air, it loses some of its water and cracks. Because no effective method has been discovered to prevent cracking, production remains very limited. Other opal occurrences are in Brazil, Honduras, Nicaragua, Guatemala, Japan, and Ireland.

Evaluation

THE PLAY OF COLORS IS MOST IMPORTANT TO THE value of an opal. Fine opals exhibit bright, intense colors. No dead patches should be present. Black opals are more valued than white. Of the types of color patterns, the harlequin is the most valuable. Fire opals without play of color are judged by the beauty of their color and transparency. Red opals are more valued than yellow and brown.

Some white opals from Australia are treated to make them black. After being soaked in sugar solution, they are immersed in sulphuric acid, which carbonizes the sugar, blackening the stone. Some Mexican opals have been turned black by smoke treatment in a mixture of charcoal and cow manure. Plastic and silica-based polymers, with or without dye, have been used to impregnate Brazilian, Mexican, and Idaho opals, significantly improving their appearance.

Opal too thin to be used in jewelry is made into doublets. A thin piece of gem-quality opal is cemented to a piece of common opal, chalcedony, or glass. If an opal doublet is covered with a protective piece of colorless quartz, it becomes a triplet, which is more durable than a doublet.

(Opposite) An opalized clam weighing 69.00 cts. from Coober Pedy, Australia.

(Below) Opal carving of a leaf from rough found in Stuart Range, South Australia, measuring 6.3 cm (2 1/2 in.) in length.

OPAL IMITATIONS, SUBSTITUTES, AND SYNTHETICS

Glass and plastic are used to imitate opal, but do so only poorly. No natural mineral resembles opal, with the possible exception of labradorite feldspar. Synthetic opals were first produced commercially in France by P. Gilson in 1972 and are successful.

Feldspar

Minerals of the feldspar group constitute over half of the Earth's crust, but nature only rarely yields them as gemstones. Remarkable iridescence is the hallmark of the best-known varieties: moonstone and labradorite. The blue shimmer of a fine moonstone forms a subtle but beckoning adornment in soft illumination, whereas laboradorite's color flash, like the peacock's tail feathers, is arresting. Of the latter, Ralph Waldo Emerson said in *Experience:* "A man is like a bit of labrador spar, which has no luster as you turn it in your hand until you come to a particular angle; then it shows deep and beautiful colors."

A polished labradorite slice measuring 7.6 cm (3 in.) long and a 3.2 cm (1 1/4 in.) diameter disk, both from Labrador, Canada.

Properties

IRIDESCENCE AND COLOR ARE THE SOURCE OF THE feldspars' gemstone appeal. They have little brilliance, and crystals are known for their cleavages. The term *feldspar* stems from these cleavages; it means "field spar." The Anglo-Saxon *spar* refers to easily cleaved minerals such as calcite, fluorite, and feldspar.

The iridescence is caused by scattering of light from thin layers in the gemstone; these layers are a second feldspar that develops by internal chemical separation during geologic cooling of an initially single feldspar. Light scattering from the layers results in pure iridescent colors (in labradorite, called "labradorescence" or "schiller") from red to blue or in a broad blue white to yellow white spectrum (in moonstone). Peristerite, intermediate in iridescence, gets its name from the Greek *peristera*, meaning "pigeon stone," in allusion to the color of the bird's neck feathers. Sunstone, also known as aventurine feldspar, reflects internal gold spangles.

Visible intergrowths produce translucency or opacity rather than iridescence in most feldspars, and most are usually not strongly colored. Moonstones are colorless to gray or yellow and semitransparent to translucent. Gem orthoclase is transparent and yellow. Labradorite is usually gray and opaque, but rare transparent crystals are occasionally found. Amazonite is an opaque feldspar with vivid green to blue green color. Translucent feldspars are carved or cut *en cabochon*; the rare transparent material is faceted for collectors.

Historic Notes

AMAZONITE (NAMED AFTER THE AMAZON RIVER) WAS widely used in Egyptian, Sudanese, Mesopotamian, and Indian jewelry; some examples date back to the third millennium B.C. The twenty-seventh chapter of the Egyptian *Book of the Dead* was engraved on this feldspar. A carved scarab and an amazonite-inlaid ring were among the jewels of Tutankhamen (reigned 1361-1352 B.C.). Amazonite was treasured by the Hebrews, and it is generally accepted that the third stone in Moses' breastplate was amazonite. In Central and South America, adornments in pre-Columbian times contained amazonite.

Moonstone appeared in Roman jewelry in about A.D. 100 and even earlier in Oriental adornment. The gemstone was a favorite of Art Nouveau jewelers, and Cartier and Tiffany creations frequently contained the gem.

Labradorite was used in decoration by the Red Paint people of Maine long before the year

---

FELDSPAR DATA

A mineral group forming two distinct compositional series (solid solutions) of alkali alumino-silicates

Plagioclase Series:	$CaAl_2Si_2O_8$ to $NaAlSi_3O_8$
Alkali Feldspar Series:	$KAlSi_3O_8$ to $NaAlSi_3O_8$
Crystal symmetry:	*Monoclinic or triclinic*
Cleavage:	*Two perfect at right angles; imperfect in a third direction*
Hardness:	*6-6.5*
Specific gravity:	*2.55-2.76*
R.I.:	*1.518-1.588 (low)*
Special optical properties:	*Light scattering and iridescence*

(Left) Labradorites ranging in weight from 2.09 to 3.01 cts., from Clear Lake, Oregon.

(Below) Moonstone intaglios of three siblings carved by noted engraver Ottavio Negri (average, 2 cm high). The moonstone is from Sri Lanka. The central intaglio is enlarged to show details.

Feldspar Gemstones

For varieties, the appropriate mineral name is given in parentheses.

PLAGIOCLASES

Labradorite:	*Middle of series—colorful iridescence, also transparent stones in yellow, orange, red, green*
Sunstone (oligoclase):	*Near Na end—gold spangles from oriented inclusions of hematite*
Peristerite (albite):	*Near Na end—blue white iridescence*

ALKALI FELDSPARS

Orthoclase:	*At K end—transparent gemstone, pale to bright yellow from iron substitution for aluminum*
Amazonite (microcline):	*At K end—yellow green to greenish blue, opaque; color from natural irradiation of microcline containing lead and water impurities*
Moonstone (orthoclase):	*Near K end—blue white to white iridescence*

1000. It was "found" by Moravian missionaries in 1770 in Labrador and named for the locality.

In the late eighteenth and nineteenth centuries, two important deposits of sunstone feldspar were found in Russia; as a result, the gem had extensive use in Russian jewelry. When sunstone deposits were found in Norway in 1850, the gem became increasingly popular in Europe.

Legends and Lore

AMAZONITE WAS A POPULAR AMULET AMONG ANcient Egyptians. According to Pliny, the Assyrians considered it the gem of Belus, their most revered god, and used it in religious rituals.

In India, moonstone was sacred and also had a special significance for lovers; if they placed it in their mouths when the moon was full, they could foresee their future. In Europe, Marbode's eleventh-century lapidary reported that the gem could bring about lovers' reconciliation. Geronimo Cardano wrote in the sixteenth century that moonstone drives sleepiness away.

Occurrences

FELDSPARS CONSTITUTE SUBSTANTIAL PORTIONS OF many igneous and metamorphic rocks. Gem varieties result from the rare geologic conditions that produce clean large grains, particularly in pegmatites and ancient deep crustal rocks.

Important localities for amazonite are in India, Brazil, Quebec in Canada, the Malagasy Republic, the Soviet Union, South Africa, and Colorado and Virginia. The best-quality moonstones came from a dike at Meetiygoda in southern Sri Lanka; this source is now exhausted. Moonstones are found in the gravels of Sri Lanka and Burma as a byproduct of ruby and sapphire mining; Madras, India, produces a less valuable quality—almost opaque and yellowish, reddish brown, or grayish blue. The finest-quality peristerites are found in Ontario and Quebec in Canada and in Kenya. Norway and the Soviet Union continue to be the sources of sunstone, and Labrador and Finland are the principal source of iridescent labradorite. Transparent, facetable labradorite is found in Mexico and in Utah, Oregon, California, and Nevada.

Evaluation

MOONSTONE IS THE MOST VALUABLE FELDSPAR. FINEquality moonstone is semitransparent and flawless and exhibits a broad blue sheen. Bright-colored amazonite is the most desirable. To be of fine quality, labradorite must display intense iridescent colors. Spectrolite is a trade name for the Finnish material. Sunstones that are semitransparent and show a pleasing reddish or yellow orange glow are the most desirable. A popular imitation, marketed as goldstone, is glass with copper inclusions.

(Opposite) Amazonite crystal measuring 6 cm (2 3/8 in.) across from the Lake George area in Colorado and cabochons carved with floral designs, with weights ranging from 18.0 to 29.9 cts., from Amelia Court House, Virginia.

GEMSTONES CONFUSED WITH FELDSPAR	
Moonstone:	*Quartz, chalcedony, and opal*
Amazonite:	*Jade and turquoise*
Labradorite:	*Opal*

Jade

The term *jade* for the ornamental stone most identified with China is a total misnomer. In the sixteenth century, Spanish conquistadors learned of a stone worn by Mesoamericans as an amulet to cure colic and similar maladies. The Spanish called it *piedra de yjada* (in Latin, *lapis nephrictus*), meaning "stone of the loin," and brought fine examples back to Europe. In translation from Spanish to French, the phrase was misprinted as *pierre le jade*.

In the mid-seventeenth century, the New World sources had disappeared, and Europeans forgot the material but not the name; they applied it to the stone of numerous carvings arriving from China. In 1780, geologist A.G. Werner described the traditional carving material and labeled it *nephrite*, after the Latin term. In 1863, French chemist Augustine Damour chemically analyzed a Chinese carving of Burmese stone and found that it was different from the Chinese nephrite. He labeled the material *jadeite*, derived from *jade*. In 1881, he discovered that Burmese jadeite and the original Mesoamerican material were identical. Nevertheless, the common term persists for both substances; jadeite and nephrite share the common name "jade." To make matters even more complicated, other stones that appear similar or have been used in a similar manner in ancient cultures are also simply called "jade." Such is the confusion with the most important ornamental gemstone.

Vessel with cover and hanging chain, 20.5 cm (8 1/16 in.) high, carved from a single piece of nephrite, mutton-fat jade, during the reign of Ch'ien Lung.

Jadeite cabochons from Burma (nine smaller stones) and Guatemala (two larger stones), with weights ranging from 6.38 to 28.34 cts., displayed on 20-kg (45-lb.) jadeite boulder from Burma.

JADE DATA

Both nephrite and jadeite jade are rocks composed of essentially a single mineral: tremolite or actinolite in nephrite and jadeite in the other. For rocks, crystal symmetry and cleavage are meaningless.

	TREMOLITE/ACTINOLITE (NEPHRITE)	JADEITE (JADEITE JADE)
Composition:	Calcium magnesium silicate	Sodium aluminum silicate
Formula:	$Ca_2(Mg,Fe)_5(Si_4O_{11})_2(OH)_2$	$NaAlSi_2O_6$
Hardness:	6	6.5-7
Specific gravity:	2.9-3.1	3.1-3.5
R.I.:	1.62 (average)	1.66 (average)

Properties

THE SPECIAL QUALITY THAT NEPHRITE AND JADEITE jade share is exceptional durability; nephrite is one of the toughest known substances. Both rarely yield to a hammer blow—a convenient field identification technique (obviously not suggested for art or artifacts). This property means that jade can be carved into remarkably fine and intricate forms with minimal risk of breaking.

Nephrite owes its exceptional toughness to a solid feltlike structure of intergrown microscopic fibrous crystals. Jadeite, slightly less durable, forms larger prismatic crystals that interlock and create a strong network. Both materials accept a fine polish because of their compactness, though nephrite's polished surface often has many small depressions, like an orange peel.

Colors and patterns are quite variable for both nephrite and jadeite. Veins, clots, zoning, and deformation can produce color variations and juxtapositions. Individual colors are due to substitutions of elements in the major constituent mineral or to "contaminant" minerals in the rock. Boulders of both nephrite and jadeite, particularly the green varieties, frequently have a tan- to ochre-colored rind due to oxidation of their constituent iron.

JADE COLORS AND THEIR CAUSES

NEPHRITE

White:	*Essentially pure tremolite, very little iron; sometimes called "mutton-fat jade."*
Deep green:	*Iron; "spinach green jade" from Siberia has blotches caused by graphite inclusions.*
Creamy brown:	*The color of this stone, sometimes called* **tomb jade,** *was once attributed to the action of heat on lime impurities but research indicates it is the result of reactions between fluids in mummies and jade, both sealed in sarcophagi.*

JADEITE

White:	*Pure jadeite.*
Leafy and blue green:	*Iron.*
Emerald green:	*Chromium; Imperial jade is the finest translucent variety.*
Lavender:	*Manganese and iron.*
Dark blue green and greenish black:	*Iron in omphacite (a calcium-rich jadeitic pyroxene) and aegerine—called "chloromelanite," a term now invalid in mineralogy.*
Deep emerald-green:	*Due to substantial amounts of the mineral kosmochlor, $NaCrSi_2O_6$; this jade variety is called* **mawsitsit** *or* **tawmawite.**

Historic Notes

BOTH JADES SHARE A UTILITARIAN BEGINNING. THE quality that drew primitive people's attention to them was their singular toughness—in this sense, we can consider them the same. Jade was the raw material for celts (choppers), axes, and clubs. One could fashion a thin, strong edge that retained its sharpness. As cultures developed, jade became a substance valued for its beauty. Thus the concept of jade, regardless of the material or name, became comparable around the world.

Jade has had its longest and most continuous history in China, nephrite being the principal jade used. According to folklore, Huang Ti in the twenty-seventh century B.C. had jade weapons and bestowed jade tablets upon officials to confer rank and authority. By the end of the Chou Dynasty (255 B.C.), carving design had reached maturity, and during the reign of Ch'ien Lung (A.D. 1736-1795), technical skill in carving achieved the highest level.

Jade has played a part in almost every aspect of Chinese life—as tools, currency, awards for statesmen, visiting ambassadors, and war heroes. Some of the earliest records of events are inscribed nephrite tablets. Ceremonial libation vessels, incense burners, and marriage

bowls were carved from nephrite; and it was the material for innumerable personal ornaments, including beads and pendants inscribed with poetry and worn as talismans.

For the Chinese, jade was not only pleasing to the eye but also to the ear and sense of touch. Musical instruments carved from jade have been used for rituals since ancient times, and rounded and well-polished "buttons" were carried in the sleeves for fingering until the end of the nineteenth century.

Jadeite jade was highly valued by the Olmecs, Mayas, Toltecs, Mixtecs, Zapotecs, and Aztecs. Carbon 14 dating of wood fragments found with jadeite artifacts in Mexico provides a date of use by the Olmecs around 1500 B.C. Jadeite was typically carved in the form of jaguars and decorated celts for ceremonial purposes. The numerous jade artifacts found in tombs include earplugs, diadems, necklaces, pendants, bracelets, masks, and statues of the sun god. The Spanish conquistadors completely destroyed the art of jade carving in America, and soon after the Conquest, the jade sources were lost.

The Maoris of New Zealand used nephrite, starting in about A.D. 1000, first as tools and weapons and later for amulets and decorations.

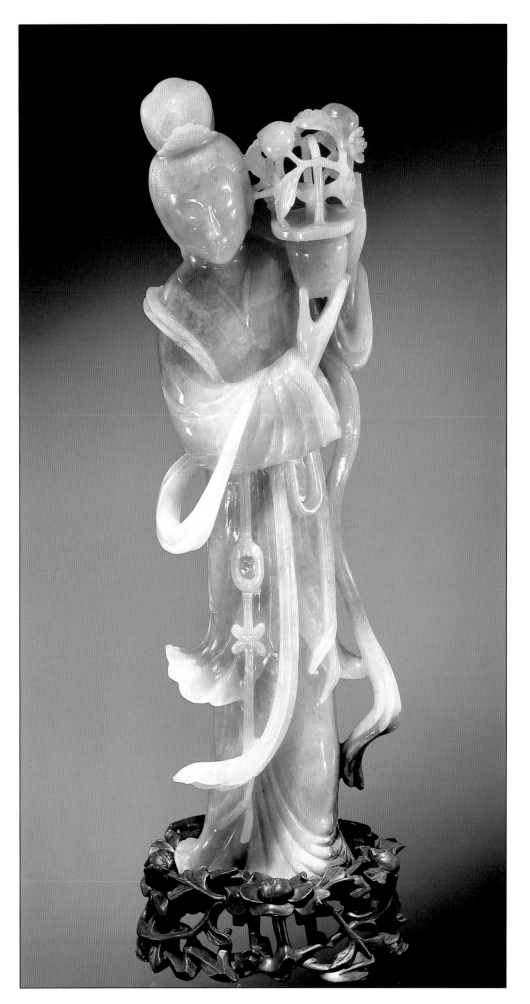

(Left) Figure of Quan-yin carved from Burmese jadeite in China during the nineteenth century. It is 28 cm (11 in.) high without the stand.

(Opposite) Olmec axe (1200-500 B.C.) of jadeite jade from Oaxaca, Mexico, 27.9 cm (11 in.) in height and weighing 15.5 lbs.

Legends and Lore

SINCE THE BEGINNING OF THEIR HISTORY, THE CHI-
nese have esteemed nephrite more than any
other gemstone. From neolithic times until the
beginning of the twentieth century, carved pi
(flat discs with a central hole) were used to worship heaven. According to a 1596 Chinese encyclopedia, drinking a mixture of jade, rice, and dew
water strengthens the muscles, hardens the
bones, calms the mind, enriches the flesh, and pu-
rifies the blood. One who takes it long enough
can endure heat, cold, hunger, and thirst.

Jade was equally important after death. An
elaborate burial shroud made of 2,156 jade tablets
sewn together with threads of gold covered the
princess Tou Wan (second century B.C.). Carved
amulets were put in the deceased's mouth, and
amulets, insignias of rank, and favorite pieces
were placed on different parts of the body and
clothing. These "tomb jades" were offerings to
the gods, but the durable stone was also believed
to protect the body from decay.

In the pre-Columbian civilizations of Mexico
and Central America, jade had great talismanic
power as well. A piece of jade in the mouth of a
dead nobleman was believed to serve as a heart
in the afterlife. Powdered and mixed with herbs,
jade was used as a treatment for fractured
skulls, different fevers, and even reviving the
dying.

The Maoris of New Zealand also revered jade
as a powerful talisman. Typical are the hei-tiki
pendants, which are grotesque human faces or
forms that were passed down to the male heirs
from generation to generation.

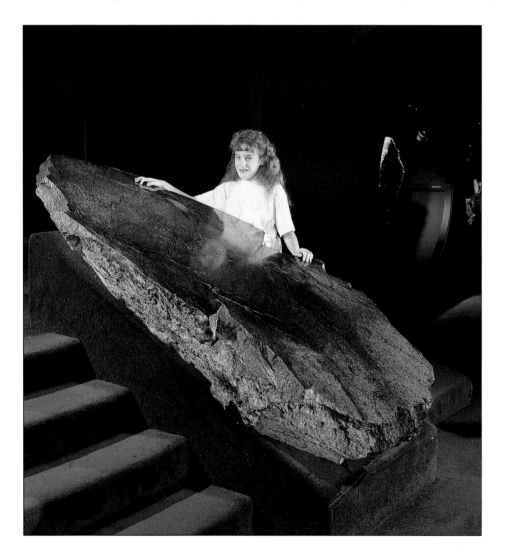

(Left) The largest nephrite
boulder ever recorded from Europe weighs 2144 kg (4727 lb.)
and has been polished on one
side by Tiffany & Co. George F.
Kunz, enroute to Russia in
1899, heard that nephrite
might be found at Jordansmuhl
in Silesia (now Jordanow,
Poland). He arrived at the
quarry at 6 a.m. and breakfast-
ed with the owner, who provided
him with a cart and workers.
Kunz found the piece, and the
quarry owner gave it to him
as the discoverer's right. (On
loan from The Metropolitan
Museum of Art.)

(Opposite) Nephrite pi disc
measuring 31 cm (12 1/4 in.)
across from Ming Dynasty
(1368-1644). The pi is the
symbol of heaven and one of the
most important ritual jades.
At burials, it was placed under
the body of the deceased.

Occurrences

BOTH NEPHRITE AND JADEITE JADE ARE METAMORPHIC rocks that result from chemical reactions between serpentinites (serpentine rock) and adjacent or embedded rock, like granite. Jadeite rock is very rare because its formation also requires conditions of considerable depth of burial (high pressure) that are infrequently preserved geologically. The durability of the jades results in their survival as stream cobbles and boulders, typically the first finds of a deposit.

Canada's British Columbia is the world's major supplier of nephrite. Here, grayish green nephrite is found, mostly along the Fraser River. Taiwan and China now use British Columbian jade.

Alaska, California, and Wyoming are also sources of nephrite. Jade Mountain in Alaska was located in 1886. The deposits are huge, but remoteness and Arctic conditions limit exploitation. South-central Wyoming has the best-quality nephrite in the Western Hemisphere, but the supply is now severely depleted.

In New Zealand, nephrite is found on South Island, both *in situ* and as pebbles and boulders in the streams. The town of Hokitika is the jade center of New Zealand.

Eastern Turkestan (now Xinjiang Province in China) is the oldest known source of nephrite, mentioned in writings from the first century B.C. For millennia, this was the source of China's nephrite. Other occurrences of nephrite are in the Soviet Union, Taiwan, Poland, and India.

Burma is the main source of jadeite and the only significant source of Imperial jade. It may be one of the oldest sources as well, for prehistoric jadeite instruments have been found in the Mogok region, possibly fashioned from pebbles and boulders recovered from the Uru River and other streams. Jadeite *in situ* was not discovered until the 1870s. The mines are nationalized, but miners smuggle much of the better-quality jadeite to Thai border towns. From there, it makes its way to Bangkok and ultimately Hong Kong. Jadeite is newly being smuggled directly to China's Yunnan Province.

Jadeite is also produced commercially in Guatemala and the Soviet Union; some is found in San Benito County in California and near Kotaki in Japan.

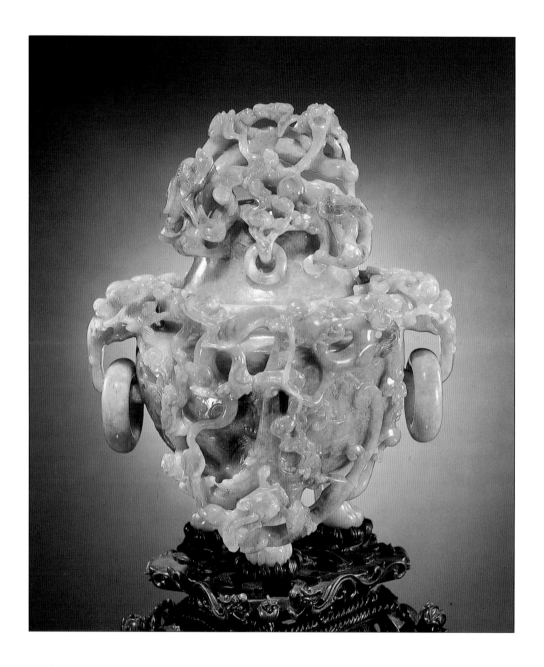

Jadite incense burner, 18 cm (7 in.) high, from the reign of Ch'ien Lung, part of a three-piece altar set.

Evaluation

THE DIFFERENCES IN QUALITY AND PRICES OF JADE are great. Color and translucency are the major considerations in evaluating both nephrite and jadeite.

The rarest and most valued color for jadeite is pure, even, and intense emerald green. When this color is combined with maximum translucency and smooth, uniform texture, the stone—known as Imperial jade—commands an extremely high price. Next in value is lavender. A jade piece has a high value if the color is pure, intense, and uniform even if it is almost opaque.

Sometimes jade is dyed green or lavender. The dyes are not always permanent, and the green frequently fades.

As a gemstone, jadeite commands substantially higher prices than nephrite. Design, craftsmanship, and antiquity are the major considerations in evaluating carvings.

Jade is imitated with mounted jade triplets, glass, and plastic. Many jade substitutes are on the market, and many other carving materials are readily confused with jade. Serpentine is probably the most common substitute.

JADE SUBSTITUTES AND THEIR TRADE NAMES

Bowenite (gem serpentine): Korean or Immature jade
Amazonite feldspar: Amazon and Colorado jade
Varieties of green grossular garnet: Transvaal jade
Aventurine quartz: Indian jade
Mixture of idocrase and grossular: American jade or Californite
Soapstone: Fukien, Manchurian, or Hunan jade
Green jasper: Swiss or Oregon jade
Green-dyed calcite: Mexican jade
Chrysoprase: Australian jade

Serpentine vase carved from Mongolian material, 16.7 cm (6 9/16 in.). Serpentine is commonly mistaken for jade.

Quartz

Quartz is a very common mineral and is easily recognized because it is so frequently found as transparent, well-formed crystals. It comes in a number of colored varieties—amethyst, citrine, rose quartz—but the colorless variety epitomizes the popular concept of crystal. The beauty and symmetry of the pointed "hexagonal" crystals and their water-clear transparency captivate the eye. It is no wonder that this natural gem has had great significance in many cultures throughout human history. Quartz crystals are among the earliest talismans; beads and seals were the first crystalline objects to be fashioned, and "gazing balls" with mystic significance are virtually synonymous with rock crystal. Whether as a crystal gemstone or in polished form, quartz can be found in the earliest prehistoric grave or the most modern collector's cabinet. The recent "New Age" attention to transcendental perceptions about quartz revives an ancient tradition.

The rock crystal statue of Atlas holding up the world is 12 cm (4 5/8 in.) in height. It was carved during the last century in Russia from a crystal found in the Ural Mountains.

Properties

THE WIDESPREAD AVAILABILITY (AND THUS MODERATE cost) of large, clear pieces in an array of colors provides quartz's appeal as a gemstone; otherwise, it has low brilliance and fire. Quartz is a remarkably pure mineral, but its coloration does require chemical impurities, although only a little—less than one impurity per thousand silicon atoms. Also, irradiation by natural or artificial means is necessary to produce both amethyst and smoky to black quartz; a large amount of the

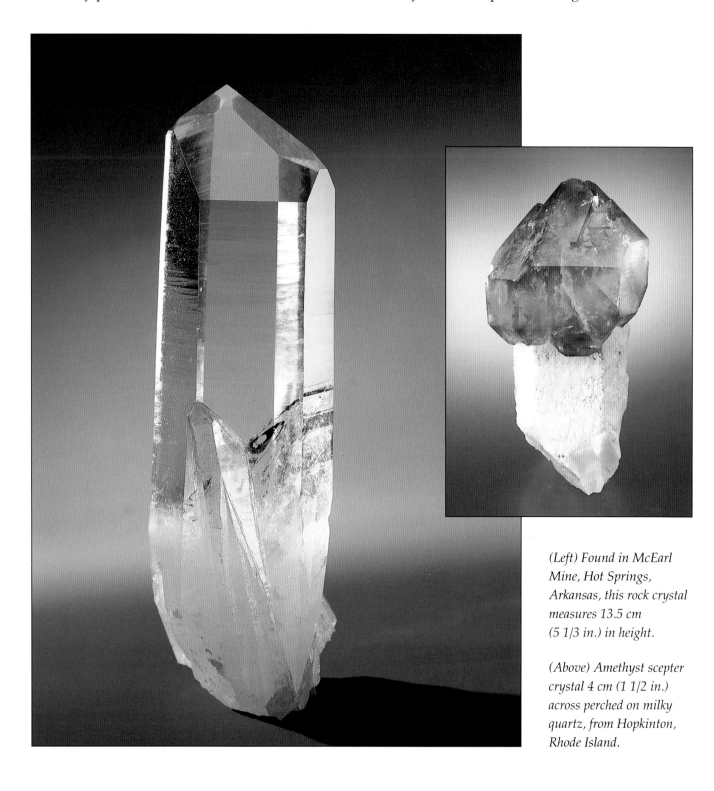

(Left) Found in McEarl Mine, Hot Springs, Arkansas, this rock crystal measures 13.5 cm (5 1/3 in.) in height.

(Above) Amethyst scepter crystal 4 cm (1 1/2 in.) across perched on milky quartz, from Hopkinton, Rhode Island.

QUARTZ DATA

Silicon oxide or silica:	*SiO_2*
Crystal symmetry:	*Trigonal*
Cleavage:	*None*
Hardness:	*7*
Specific gravity:	*2.65*
R.I.:	*1.544-1.553 (moderate)*
Dispersion:	*Low*

---

available smoky quartz is artificially irradiated rock crystal. Similarly, citrine, which is rare in nature, is commercially created by heat-treating natural amethyst.

Quartz has a strong framework crystal structure that makes it hard and free from cleavage—a durable material. It is also a common component of dust, which is the abrasive enemy of all gemstones; this is why quartz's hardness is considered the division between soft and hard gems—those softer or harder than quartz.

Inclusions in quartz are responsible for some very interesting varieties with banded or spangly reflections or just color. Fibers are found in rutilated quartz, cat's eye, and sagenite. In hawk's eye, the blue color comes from blue asbestos veins that have been infiltrated and replaced by quartz; if the asbestos breaks down totally, an iron oxide residue imparts the bronze color of tiger's eye. Small particles, fractures, and fluids are responsible for aventurine, iris quartz, and milky quartz.

Quartz crystals are usually elongate hexagonal-looking prisms capped by a "hexagonal pyramid." However, the crystals only have threefold symmetry. This fact is well demonstrated by the three-bladed pinwheel effect in some amethysts.

Quartz, alone with tourmaline among gemstones, lacks a center of symmetry in its crystal structure; this condition makes it piezoelectric. When pressure is applied across opposing prism faces, they develop opposite charges; relaxation reverses the effect. The property has important application in electronics, but there is no substantiated scientific evidence that humans can directly sense electronic vibrations in quartz.

GEMSTONE QUARTZ VARIETIES, COLORS, AND COLOR SOURCES

Rock crystal:	*Colorless*
Amethyst:	*Purple—iron + aluminum + irradiation*
Citrine:	*Yellow to amber—iron*
Morion:	*Black—aluminum + irradiation*
Smoky quartz or cairngorm:	*Smoky gray to brown—aluminum + irradiation*
Rose quartz:	*Translucent pink—titanium or inclusions*
Green quartz, or praziolite:	*Green—iron + heating*

(Above) Amethyst brooch set with diamonds and a 45.71-ct ametrine (trystine), from Puerto Suarez, Bolivia. Ametrine is bicolor amethyst-citrine, discovered in 1977.

(Left) "Pinwheel" amethyst weighing 41.17 cts., from Brazil. It shows quartz's trigonal symmetry.

(Opposite) An amethyst crystal group measuring 7.5 cm (3 in.) across, from Thunder Bay, Ontario, Canada.

INCLUSIONS IN QUARTZES

Milky quartz:	*White—fluids, mainly water*
Aventurine:	*Green or brick red—chromian mica or hematite flakes*
Rutilated quartz:	*Golden reflecting—rutile needles*
Iris quartz:	*Iridescence—numerous small cracks*
Sagenite (or Venus hair, Thetis hair):	*A netlike pattern of needles—rutile, black tourmaline, green actinolite, or epidote*
Cat's eye:	*Chatoyancy in several color varieties—fibers of rutile*
Tiger's eye:	*Bronze chatoyancy—brown iron oxides from asbestos weathering*
Hawk's eye:	*Blue chatoyancy—blue asbestos*

H*istoric* N*otes*

Q*UARTZ* DERIVES FROM THE S*LAVIC* *KWARDY*, MEAN-ing "hard." The Latinized *quarzum* was first recorded in the sixteenth century by the German scholar Agricola, who made the first scientific classification of minerals. According to him, the term was used by the Bohemian miners of Joachimstal (now Jachimov, Czechoslovakia).

Rock crystal objects have been found with re-mains of prehistoric man (75,000 B.C.) in France, Switzerland, and Spain. Cylinder seals of rock crys-tal appeared in the Near East by the fourth millen-nium B.C. As an amulet and a decorative stone, it found use in Egypt before 3100 B.C. The ancient Greeks and Romans used it extensively in jewelry,

valuing its flawless transparency. The Greeks be-lieved that the gemstone was water frozen by the gods to remain forever ice; our term *crystal* derives from the Greek *krystallos,* meaning "ice."

During the Middle Ages and Renaissance in Europe, rock crystal vessels were carved for royal and ecclesiastical use, and for centuries the Jap-anese and Chinese carved the material, as did the Mayas, pre-Aztecs, Aztecs, and Incas on the other side of the world.

Amethyst was used as a decorative stone be-fore 25,000 B.C. in France and has been found with the remains of neolithic man in different parts of Europe. Before 3100 B.C. in Egypt, beads, amulets, and seals were made of this gemstone, and it was highly valued in ancient Greek and Roman societies. An amethyst was the ninth stone in the breastplate of the high priest of Israel and one of the ten stones on which the names of the tribes of Israel were engraved.

In medieval times, amethyst graced royal crowns and bishops' rings. A huge round amethyst adorns the British royal scepter, set for the coronation of James II (1633-1701), and another remarkable amethyst surmounts the sovereign orb. Brazilian amethysts appeared on the European market in 1727 and became highly fashionable and expensive. Amethyst was very popular during the eighteenth century in France and England. A necklace of amethysts was purchased at a very high price for Queen Charlotte (1744-1818), wife of George III of England. Soon after, the price declined as amethysts from Ural Mountains deposits (discovered in 1799) and Brazil increased the supply.

Smoky quartz was used by the Sumerians in the valley of the Euphrates and by the Egyptians before 3100 B.C. Beads surviving from Roman times are fairly frequent. The stone was popular with the Navajo and other Native Americans. Smoky quartz is also called "cairngorm" from the Cairngorm Mountains in Scotland; the stones have been set into brooches and the handles of dirks.

Rose quartz, named for its pink to rose color, was first used by the Assyrians (800-600 B.C.) and later by the Romans, but it was not common in the jewelry of the ancient world. Today it is very popular for bead necklaces, small carvings, and cabochons.

Citrine was considered a gem during the Hellenistic Age in Greece (323-280 B.C.) and was moderately popular for intaglios and cabochon ring stones through the first and second centuries A.D. in Greece and Rome. It has had ongoing use in jewelry but has never achieved the prominence of amethyst. The name derives from the French *citron,* meaning "lemon," an allusion to its color. Agricola applied the term to the yellow variety of quartz in the sixteenth century.

Legends and Lore

AN ANCIENT GREEK MYTH RELATES THAT THE GOD Bacchus, to avenge an insult, declared that the first person he met would be devoured by his tigers. This person happened to be Amethyst, on her way to worship at the shrine of Diana. As the beasts sprang, Diana turned the girl into a clear, transparent crystal. Repenting, Bacchus poured juice of grapes as a libation over the stone, thus giving the gem its beautiful purple color. The Greeks believed that amethyst would prevent intoxication, and, in legend, it also calmed anger and relieved frustrated passion.

In medieval Europe, amethyst was worn as a soldier's amulet to preserve him in battle. In addition, amethyst made men shrewd in business matters, according to Camillus Leonardus, a sixteenth-century authority on precious stones.

The allure of rock crystal has been virtually universal. The Japanese regarded it as "the perfect jewel, tama": a symbol of purity, the infinity of space, patience, and perseverance. In places as far apart as North America and Burma, rock crystal has been considered a living entity. Native American Cherokee Indians not only used it as a talisman for hunting, they periodically "fed" the stone by rubbing it with deer's blood; the crystal was similarly nourished by the Burmese.

Crystal balls that the Crusaders brought from the Near East were reputed to possess magical powers. Until the end of the last century, rock crystal balls have been employed to cure diseases of cattle in Ireland and Scotland. Quartz crystal has attained enormous recent popularity from the belief that it is a psychic amplifier.

(Left) Quartz varieties including rock crystal, smoky quartz, citrine, amethyst, rose quartz, and green quartz. Weights range from 13.16 to 489.85 cts. The gems come from various localities.

(Below) Amethysts of 163.50 cts. and 88.20 cts., both from the Ural Mountains in the Soviet Union.

(Opposite) Russian rock crystal carving from the nineteenth century, measuring 13.2 cm (5 1/4 in.).

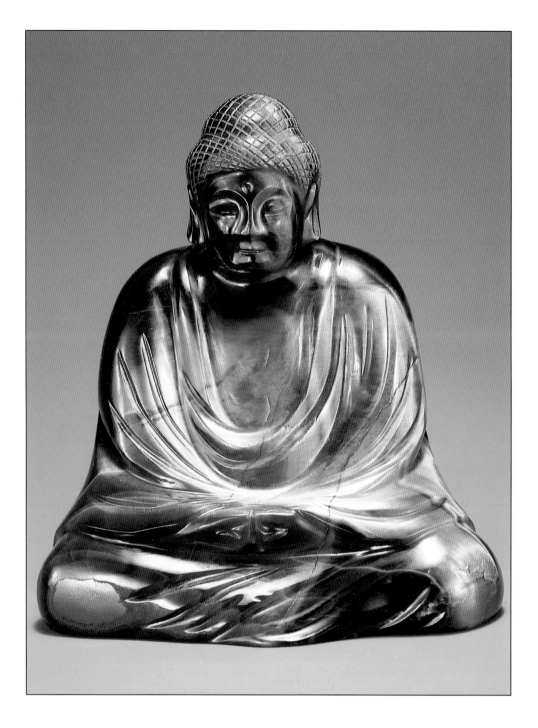

Tiger's eye quartz carving of a seated Buddah from South Africa, 8 cm high (3 1/8 in.).

Occurrences

QUARTZ FORMS IN A WIDE VARIETY OF ENVIRONMENTS, but gemstone crystals usually require the openings in rocks, such as veins, cavities, and pockets, to grow to perfection and adequate size. Crystal-lined pockets, called geodes, are a familiar source of quartz. In pegmatites containing quartz and sufficient radioactive minerals to provide the necessary irradiation amethyst and smoky quartz will develop.

There are many commercial sources of gem-quality rock crystal. Brazil is the principal source for all varieties of quartz. Arkansas is important for rock crystal in the United States. The most prolific producers of amethyst are Brazil and Uruguay. Amethyst is found also in Arizona and North Carolina. The major commercial source of citrine is Brazil (Minas Gerais, Goias, Esperito Santo, and Bahia).

Evaluation

AMONG THE MANY VARIETIES OF QUARTZ, AMETHYST IS the most expensive. Intense and uniform purple is the most desired. Any flaws diminish the price considerably. Amethyst may be confused with purple sapphire or spinel. It can be imitated with synthetic sapphire or glass. Synthetic amethyst is manufactured in the Soviet Union.

Clarity is *the* factor in evaluating rock crystal. The price is moderate, except for very large flawless pieces. Herkimer diamond, Arkansas diamond, Arizona diamond, Cape May diamond, Alaska diamond, and Cornish diamond are some of the misnomers used for rock crystal. Synthetic rock crystal is used in industry rather than in jewelry. Poorly formed or coated quartz crystals are polished and sold as natural crystals or "points." This practice is misleading; the quartz is natural, but the faces are not.

For rose quartz, the deeper the color and the more transparent the gem, the greater its value. Rose quartz is sometimes dyed, but the dye fades.

The value of both citrine and smoky quartz is determined by clarity and the attractiveness of their colors. Quartz of yellow and golden brown to orange brown is rare. Citrine is often sold fraudulently as topaz, whose color is richer. However, due to its lack of cleavage, citrine is tougher, wears better, and is less expensive.

Group of three intergrown rutilated quartz crystals measuring 6.7 cm (2 5/8 in.) in height, from Itabira, Minas Gerais, Brazil.

Chalcedony & Jasper

These gemstones were as highly prized by our earliest ancestors as they are by today's lapidary hobbyists. The basis of their appeal comes from the literally hundreds of colorful varieties that can be found. Both are made up of submicroscopic quartz grains—thus are varieties of quartz—and owe their bonanza of colors and patterns to included minute grains of other pigmenting minerals. Chalcedony differs from jasper in that its tiny crystals are parallel fibers rather than sugar-like grains. Distinguishing them requires a microscope, although typically chalcedony is banded and translucent. Listing all the varieties of these gemstones would be daunting to a philologist, let alone a mineralogist. Only the most important and well-known varieties of chalcedony and jasper are discussed here.

Carnelian vase carved in China; it measures 10.5 cm (4 1/8 in.) across.

Properties

THE GEMSTONE PROPERTIES OF CHALCEDONY AND jasper are the properties of quartz—good hardness and durability. As essentially superfine grained rocks, the directional properties of crystals, such as symmetry, are not visible to the naked eye.

In chalcedony the tiny quartz fibers form layers in a velvet-like pile. The layers stack up one upon the other, often producing a banded appearance as seen in the best-known chalcedony variety, agate. The fibrous structure imparts substantial toughness, too. Layers can be translucent to opaque and vary from gray to white when they are free of impurities to almost any color when they are pigmented with an appropriate impurity. Except for white layers, porosity is pronounced; the gemstones are easily dyed. Onyx, a black-and-white variety, is naturally rare but is commercially produced by soaking pale agate in a sugar solution and then carbonizing the sugar in sulfuric acid, rendering the gemstone black and white.

Jasper's granular texture makes it tough and generally more opaque than chalcedony, and jasper lacks the other's banding. While commonly red to ochre from iron oxide pigments, jasper can occur in a multitude of colors. Some materials have mixed textures of both chalcedony and jasper juxtaposed in anywhere from millimeter- to centimeter-scale patches. Gemstone varieties that show either or both textures include bloodstone and chrysoprase.

The layered texture of agates, particularly onyx and sardonyx, have made them very popular materials for carving intaglios and cameos. Cameos are usually carved with the white layer in relief and the colored layer as background. In intaglios, the figure is incised through the dark layer to reveal the white layer—or the reverse.

(Right) A polished agate slab from an unknown locality measures 18 cm (7 in.) across.

(Opposite) Carnelian in an Islamic necklace with tassels; a Chinese belt buckle measuring 6 cm (2 3/8 in.) across; seventh-century Merovingian necklace spanning 28 cm (11 in.), found in France near Soissons; and Native American bracelets.

CHALCEDONY VARIETIES

Agate:	**All forms with parallel to concentric banding, transparent to opaque.**
Bull's eye agate:	Bands form concentric circles.
Iris or fire agate:	Iridescent from thin layers of iron oxide crystals.
Onyx:	Bands are black and white—popularly miscontrued to be all black.
Sardonyx:	Bands are brown to ochre and white.
Bloodstone or heliotrope:	**Plasma with red hematite or jasper spots and blotches.**
Carnelian:	**Translucent red brown to brick red from hematite.**
Chrysoprase:	**Translucent apple green from nickel serpentine.**
Moss agate:	**Translucent light-colored body with black, brown, or green moss-looking to branchlike (dendritic) inclusions, usually dark oxides. "Mocha stone" is moss agate from a source near Mocha in Yemen.**
Plasma:	**Opaque leek to dark green from various green silicate minerals.**
Prase:	**Translucent leek green from chlorite inclusions.**
Sard:	**Translucent light to chestnut brown from iron oxides and hydroxides.**

(Left) The onyx clock face, carved cameo style, displays carved female figures. The diameter is 11.5 cm (4 1/2 in.).

(Below) Moss agate from India. The largest is 7.5 (3 in.) in diameter.

Historic Notes

THE TERM *CHALCEDONY* MAY DERIVE FROM THE AN-cient Greek port of Chalcedon. The terms *chryso-prase* and *prase* come from the Greek *chrysos* and *prase*, meaning "golden" and "leek." Carnelian derives from the Latin *cornum*, meaning "cornel berry" or "cornelian cherry." *Heliotrope* (blood-stone) derives from the Greek *helio*, meaning "sun," and *trepein*, meaning "turning." *Jasper* de-rives from the Greek *iaspis*, of Oriental origin but unknown significance.

Sard comes from the Greek Sardis, capital of Lydia in Asia Minor. *Agate* is named for the Achates (Drillo) River in Sicily, a major source of the gem, according to Theophrastus. Plasma alone is a use-derived name; the Greek word from which it comes means "something molded" or "something imitated."

The oldest jasper adornments date back to the paleolithic period. Agate has been found with the remains of Stone Age man in France (20,000-16,000 B.C.), and agate, carnelian, and chryso-prase were used by the Egyptians before 3000 B.C. Magnificent agate and jasper jewelry has been found in Harappa, one of the oldest centers of the Indus civilization. Sard was used by the Mycenaeans (1450-1100 B.C.) and the Assyrians (1400-600 B.C.). Carnelian and sard were favorite stones of Roman gem engravers. Carnelian seals have been esteemed by the Muslims; the Prophet Mohammed wore one himself. Prase was used as a gemstone in Greece in around 400 B.C. Mining of agate at around the same time in India has been documented, although the gem was probably used much earlier.

The small German towns of Idar and Oberstein were a source of agate, jasper, and other stones in Roman times, and during the fif-teenth century, an agate industry was established there. It flour-ished until early in the nineteenth century, when the mines were de-pleted, and many skilled miners and lapidaries went elsewhere. In 1827, German settlers discovered rich chalcedony deposits in Brazil and Uruguay. By 1834, Brazilian agate was being exported to Ger-many. Although Idar-Oberstein is no longer a supply source, it is renowned for the quality and artistry of its gem craft. Currently, it imports raw material from about 100 countries and employs more than 500 gem polishers and numerous en-gravers and wholesale gem dealers.

Agate cameo, its rough from Uruguay, mea-suring 4.7 cm (1 7/8 in.) in length.

Legends and Lore

As ANCIENT GEMS, THE CHALCEDONIES AND JASPERS have accrued the lore of the ages. Bloodstone preserves an owner's health and protects him or her from deception (Damigeron, first century A.D.). Sard has medicinal virtue for wounds (Epiphanius, fourth-century bishop of Salamis in Cyprus), and protects the possessor from incantations and sorcery (Marbode in the eleventh century). Chrysoprase strengthens the eyesight and relieves internal pain (eleventh-century Byzantine manuscript of Michael Psellius). Carnelian gives an owner courage in battle (Ibnu'l Baitar, botanist of the thirteenth century) and helps timid speakers become both eloquent and bold.

Perhaps the most intriguing virtue of all is noted in Volmar's thirteenth-century *Steinbüch*: a thief, sentenced to death, may escape his executioners immediately—if he puts chrysoprase in his mouth.

Occurrences

CHALCEDONY AND JASPER ARE GEOLOGICALLY COMmon, formed in cavities, cracks, and by replacement where low-temperature silica-rich waters percolate through sediments and rocks, particularly those of volcanic origin. Chalcedonies are common the world around. Brazil, Uruguay, and India produce all varieties of chalcedony and jaspers. With the exception of sard and plasma, all chalcedonies come from diverse localities in the United States.

Additional sources are: chrysoprase—Australia, Zimbabwe and the Soviet Union; carnelian—South Africa and China; agate—Mexico, Namibia, and the Malagasy Republic; jasper—Venezuela, Germany, and the Soviet Union; bloodstone—Australia.

An assortment of jaspers, chalcedonies and other ornamental stones including a heliotrope (bloodstone—green and red cylinder; a banded brown, white and pink jasper cabochon; a carnelian pendant 6 cm (2 3/8 in.) high; a faceted blue chalcedony; an obsidian bowl an onyx intaglio; as well as sodalite, prehnite, turquoise and jadeite cabochons.

Evaluation

THE ATTRACTIVENESS OF COLORS AND PATTERNS determines the value of all varieties. The naturally-colored stones have higher prices than the artifically colored. Chrysoprase is rare and the most valuable variety. Translucency is an important consideration for chrysoprase, carnelian, sard, agate, and prase. (Prase is presently rarely used in jewelry, however.)

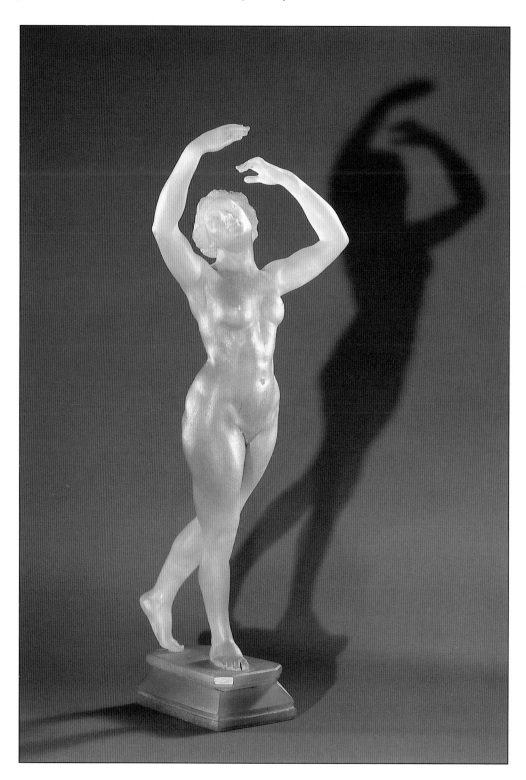

(Right) Pas de Danse, carved by G. Tonnelier, stands 21.5 cm (8 1/2 in.) tall. Its chalcedony rough is from Uruguay.

(Opposite) A chalcedony vase carved in China measures 10.6 cm (4 1/4 in.) high.

Garnet

Garnets are not just red; they come in all colors excepting blues. This is news to many, as may be the fact that new varieties of gem garnet have been discovered in the last few decades. Tsavorite was unearthed in 1968 near Kenya's Tsavo National Park and named for it by Tiffany promoters. It is a beautiful gemstone that rivals emerald but has been in short supply. And about twenty years ago in eastern Africa, a reddish orange garnet was found in the search for the purplish pink rhodolite garnet particularly desired in Japan. Attempts to sell the Japanese on the new garnet were futile, so the stone was called "malaia," a Swahili word meaning "outcast" and "prostitute." To the Africans' surprise, in the late 1970s Americans found the maligned garnet very attractive. But the name has stuck.

Spessartine crystals up to 1.5 cm (9/16 in.) across on quartz from Naugahar Province, Afghanistan, a 28.41-ct. almandine from Tanzania, and an 8.97-ct. round brilliant-cut pyrope from Macon County, North Carolina.

Properties

GARNETS ARE COLORFUL, LIVELY, AND DURABLE—A fine gemstone group, but complex. There are many varieties and many mineral species—like a fruit market with Granny Smith and Delicious apples as well as Concord and green grapes. The colors of the gemstone garnets vary with species as well as with minor substitutions of transition metals into the structure. The iron- and manganese-bearing garnets are intrinsically colored (idiochromatic), whereas those without transition elements are colorless in the pure form (allochromatic). Grossular has the greatest range of colors, and andradite has the highest brilliance and fire—particularly the superb green variety, demantoid. The mistaken concept that garnets are red derives from the predominant use of almandine and pyrope as gems.

Garnet, particularly almandine, can develop fibrous inclusions of several possible minerals in three perpendicular directions; such gemstones can show four- or six-rayed stars when fashioned as cabochons. Garnet's cubic symmetry leads to multifaced equidimensional crystals that can vary greatly in size; some small ones look like natural beads.

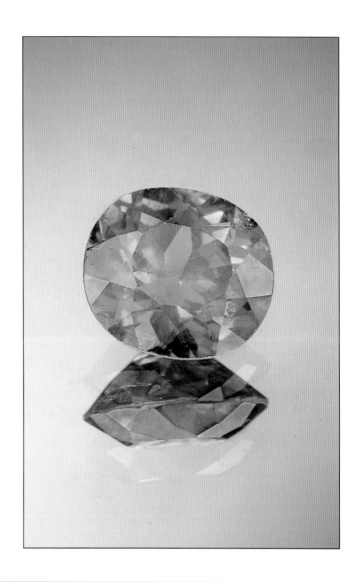

GARNET DATA

Garnet is the name of a group of silicate minerals; the gemstone garnets can be described in terms of five limiting members. There is extensive solid solution between minerals listed within each column but not between the columns.

Pyrope:	$Mg_3Al_2(SiO_4)_3$	Grossular:	$Ca_3Al_2(SiO_4)_3$
Almandine:	$Fe_3Al_2(SiO_4)_3$	Andradite:	$Ca_3Fe_2(SiO_4)_3$
Spessartine:	$Mn_3Al_2(SiO_4)_3$		

Crystal symmetry:	Cubic
Cleavage:	None
Hardness:	6.5-7.5
Specific gravity:	3.5-4.3
R.I.:	1.714-1.895 (moderate to high)
Dispersion:	Moderate

GEMSTONE GARNET SPECIES, VARIETIES, COLORS, AND SOURCES OF COLOR

SPECIES	VARIETIES	COLORS AND CAUSES
Pyrope		Colorless, pink to red from iron
	Chrome pyrope	Orange red from chromium
Almandine		Orangy red to purplish red
Pyrope-almandine		Reddish orange to red purple
	Rhodolite	Purplish red to red purple
Spessartine		Yellowish orange, redder with more iron
Almandine-spessartine		Reddish orange to orange red
Pyrope-spessartine		Greenish yellow to purple
	Malaia	Yellowish to reddish orange to brown
	Color-change garnet	Blue green in daylight to purple red in incandescent light due to vanadium and chromium
Grossular		Colorless, orange from ferrous iron; also pink, yellow, and brown
	Tsavorite	Green to yellowish green from vanadium
	Hessonite	Yellow orange to red orange from manganese and iron
Andradite		Yellowish green to orangy yellow to black
	Demantoid	Green to yellow green from chromium
	Topazolite	Yellow to orangy yellow

(Opposite) A demantoid garnet from Poldenwaja in the Ural Mountains of the Soviet Union, weighing 4.94 cts.

(Right) Spessartine crystal (modified dodecahedron) 1.5 cm (9/16 in.) across on smoky quartz. The specimen was found in Ramona, California.

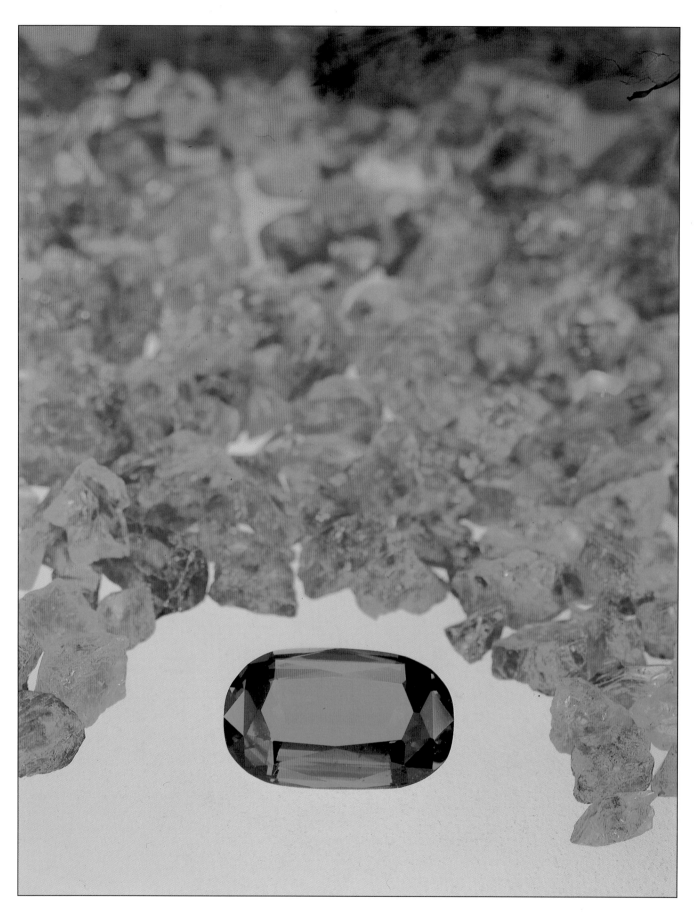

Tsavorite gem gravel and an 8.16-ct. stone, all from eastern Africa, probably Teita Hills, Kenya.

Historic Notes

GARNET DERIVES FROM THE LATIN *GRANATUM*, MEANing "pomegranate," and alludes to the crystal's red color and seedlike form. Red garnet gems date back thousands of years. Excavations of lake dwellers' graves in Czechoslovakia have uncovered garnet necklaces and suggest use of the material in the Bronze Age. Other findings indicate widespread use of the gems for beads and inlaid work in Egypt before 3100 B.C., in Sumeria around 2300 B.C., and in Sweden between 2000-1000 B.C. Garnets were the favorite stones in Greece in the fourth and third centuries B.C. and remained popular during Roman times. Garnet-inlaid jewelry has been discovered in southern Russia in graves of the second century A.D. Over 4,000 garnets decorate jewelry that was found when a seventh-century ship burial was excavated in East Anglia in 1939. Aztecs and other Native Americans used garnets in their ornaments in pre-Columbian times.

Pyrope garnets were the basis for a thriving jewelry and cutting center in Bohemia, Czechoslovakia, that started in about 1500. Until the late nineteenth century, the Bohemian deposits were the world's major source of the stone.

Rhodolite garnet from Tanzania, weighing 24.5 cts.

THE NAMES OF THE GARNETS

Pyrope: From the Greek **pyros**, *meaning "fiery" and alluding to the stone's deep red color*

Almandine: *From Alabanda, an ancient garnet source in Asia Minor (now Turkey)*

Rhodolite: *Derived from two Greek words that mean "rose stone"*

Spessartine: *Named for Spessart, the Bavarian district where the gem was first found*

Andradite: *Named after mineralogist J.B. d'Andrada, who described a variety in 1800*

Topazolite: *Similar to topaz in color*

Demantoid: *Derived from the Dutch **demant**, meaning "diamond," named for its diamond-like brilliance*

Grossular: *Derived from the botanical name of the gooseberry, **R. grossularia**, alluding to similarity between the colors of the berries and some pale green grossulars*

(Opposite) Nineteenth-century Bohemian jewelry of pyrope garnet. (One bracelet stone is misssing.)

(Above) A hessonite engraved with Christ's head, from the Vatican collection. This piece measures 3.6 cm (1 3/8 in.) in height.

(Right) Engraved almandine garnet bowl from India with a diameter of 5.5 cm (2 1/8 in.).

Legends and Lore

A SINGLE LARGE GARNET PROVIDED THE ONLY LIGHT on Noah's ark, according to the Talmud. During the Middle Ages, garnet was regarded as a gem of faith, truth, and constancy. As late as 1609, Anselmus de Boot contended that garnet drives away melancholy.

Like other red stones, garnet was considered a remedy for hemorrhage and inflammatory dis-eases and a general protection from wounds, a belief that has been revived among some New Age adherents. In contrast, some Asiatic tribes believed that garnet bullets would be more dead-ly than those of lead. Accordingly, in 1892, the Hanzas used garnet bullets (some of which have been preserved) against British troops during hostilities on the Kashmir frontier.

Occurrences

GARNETS FORM IN MANY METAMORPHIC AND SOME IG-
neous rocks. Almandine is the common metamorphic garnet; spessartine is similar, but the purest
orangy ones form in pegmatites. Pyrope crystallizes at high pressures. Grossular and andradite
form in contact metamorphic zones, particularly
next to marble.

Superb rubylike pyropes are found in dia-
mond-bearing kimberlites in South Africa and the
Soviet Union. Fine-quality but small pyropes are
found in Arizona, New Mexico, and Utah. Other
sources are eastern Africa, Australia, Brazil, and
Burma.

Major sources of almandine are India, Sri
Lanka, and Brazil. Star stones are found in Idaho
and India.

Rhodolite, more transparent than pyrope and
almandine, was originally found in Lower Creek,
North Carolina, in 1882. The major commercial
source is Tanzania; rhodolite is also found in
India, Sri Lanka, Zimbabwe, and the Malagasy
Republic.

Gemstone spessartine's rare occurrences include Brazil, Ramona, California, and Amelia
Court House, Virginia, the major source in the
late nineteenth century.

Malaia, the new variety, comes from the Umba
Valley in Tanzania. Color-change pyrope-spessar-
tine is also found in eastern Africa. Demantoid
was first found in about 1851 in placers in the
Ural Mountains. A newer deposit is in Chukotka
in the Soviet Union. Other occurrences are in
Zaire; Korea; and Val Malenco, Italy.

Kenya and Tanzania are the only sources of tsavorite. Other sources of gem grossular are Sri
Lanka (yellow, brown, pink, red); Asbestos, Canada (yellow, brown to pinkish); and Chihuahua,
Mexico (large crystals, seldom transparent).
Green, compact, fine-grained grossular containing small black specks resembles jade and frequently is sold for it. Examples are Transvaal
jade, found near Pretoria in South Africa, and material from the Yukon Territory in Canada and
California. Massive white grossular from Burma
is used for carvings and often sold as jade.

Evaluation

PURITY OF COLOR, CLARITY, AND SIZE ARE THE MOST
important considerations. Green garnets are the
most highly prized, but the market is plagued by
poor availability. Demantoid is the most valuable
of the garnets; among all gems, it is prized for its
beauty and rarity. Emerald green, transparent,
flawless stones are extremely valuable. Brownish
red garnets are less valuable than the pure red.
The price per carat for a fine-quality garnet increases with size.

Gemstones Confused with Garnets

Pyrope and **almandine:** *Red spinel and ruby. (Pyrope is occasionally marketed as Arizona ruby, Cape ruby, Elie ruby, and Fashoda ruby; all are misleading names.)*

Rhodolite: *Plum-colored sapphire and tourmaline*

Grossular: *Emerald, topaz, zircon, or jade*

Demantoid: *Green diamond or zircon*

Spessartine: *Zircon and grossular garnet*

Etched mass of spessartine garnet sprinkled with pyrite and measuring 6 cm (2 3/8 in.) across and a 98.61-ct. cut stone, from Amelia Court House, Virginia.

Pearls & Other Organic Gems

Pearl, amber, coral, and jet share an organic origin and, in that sense, form a gem group.

PEARL

Pearls are finished gems when found. Their beauty has been valued for centuries, but their popularity has varied over time. In 1916, millionaire Morton Plant wanted to purchase a magnificent rope of pearls at Cartier's for his wife. The price was $1 million! He proposed an exchange—a piece of real estate for the necklace—and Cartier agreed. In 1956, these magnificent pearls were auctioned at Parke-Bernet and brought only $151,000. The real estate is the Fifth Avenue landmark building that Cartier still occupies, one of the most valuable corners in New York City.

Chrysanthemum brooch with American fresh-water pearls and diamonds, 7.5 cm (3 in.) across. A Tiffany creation from around 1900, it was exhibited in "Tiffany: 150 Years of Gems and Jewelry" in 1988. (Courtesy of Mrs. Robert S. Weatherly, Jr.)

Properties

LUSTROUS PEARLS ARE PRODUCED BY MOLLUSCS HAV-ing a nacreous (mother of pearl) lining, in response to foreign irritants such as parasites or sand grains. Layers upon layers of nacre are deposited on the object, forming pearl's onionlike structure. Conchiolin (a horny substance) binds aragonite microcrystals together about the inclu-sion. The crystals overlap, producing a slightly irregular surface that feels rough when rubbed across the teeth, a reliable way of distinguishing natural and cultured pearls from imitations. The luster is caused by the scattering and interference of light by the concentric layers. The light inter-ference and diffraction produce an overtone color called "orient." Pearls are semitransparent to opaque and are divided into three color groups: white, black, and colored.

Pearl-bearing molluscs inhabit both salt and fresh water. Salt-water pearls are the more highly prized for jewelry. They come principally from oysters of the *Pinctada* genus. The major source of fresh-water pearls are mussels of the genus *Unio*.

Cultured pearls are produced by artificial stim-ulation of the natural process. Baby oysters ("spat") are cultured in plastic cages in protected waters. After three years, a bead of mother of pearl and a small piece of oyster mantle tissue are inserted into the body of each oyster. Nacre is se-creted around the bead by the foreign tissue. The oysters are returned to the culture cages in the sea. After three years, the oysters are recovered and the pearls removed. The largest Japanese sea-water cultured pearls have a diameter of about two-fifths of an inch.

Acids, including those from the human skin, are very damaging to pearl, as are cosmetics, per-fume, and hair sprays. Excessive dryness or hu-midity in the air shortens the life of a pearl. Since pearls are soft, jumbling them together in a box with other gems that scratch them is most de-structive. Pearl weight is measured in grains rather than carats: 1 grain = 0.25 carat.

PEARL DATA

Pearls are built up from layers of nacre.

Nacre composition: Aragonite, $CaCO_3$ (82-86%), conchiolin — a horny organic substance (10-14%), and water, H_2O (2%).

Luster: Pearly.

Cleavage: None; pearls are very tough.

Hardness: 2.5 to 4.5.

Pearl Colors and Shapes

COLOR—*THE SUM OF BODY COLOR PLUS OVERTONE COLOR OR ORIENT.*

White: *White—white body color, no overtone*

Cream—cream body color, no overtone

Light rosé—white body color, pinkish overtone

Cream rosé—cream body color, deep rose overtone

Fancy—cream body color, rose and blue overtones

Black: *Black, gray, bronze, dark blue, blue green, green body colors with or without metallic overtones*

Colored: *Red, purple, yellow, violet, blue, or green body color—more common in freshwater pearls*

SHAPES

Round, pear, drop, egg, button (with flat back), baroque (irregularly shaped), blister (attached to shell); seed (unsymmetrical, less than 0.25 grain)

Historic Notes

By 2200 B.C., PEARLS WERE TAX AND TRIBUTE IN China; an Oriental dictionary written before 1000 B.C. specifies pearl as a product of western provinces. Embroidered on costumes and made into ropes and ornaments in ancient Persia (Iran), pearls were the privilege of royalty. In Rome, they were the most admired gems and so frequently worn that the philosopher Seneca (c. 54 B.C.-A.D. 39) criticized women for wearing too many of them.

Throughout the Middle Ages in Europe, pearls were royal gems exclusively, although the Crusaders brought scores of them from the Orient. When Catherine de Medici came to France to marry Henry, Duke of Orleans, in 1532, she brought six strings of fine pearls and twenty-five large single pearls, which she later presented to Mary Stuart (1542-1587). After Mary's death, the Medici pearls were purchased for a trifle by Elizabeth I (1533-1603). In all her portraits, Elizabeth is accoutered with pearls. Men also wore pearls, as demonstrated by royal portraits of the period. In 1612, an edict of the Duke of Saxony stated that the nobility were not to wear dresses embroidered with pearls, and professors and doctors of the universities and their wives were not to use

any pearl jewelry. During the late Renaissance, baroque pearl pendants in the forms of dragons, mermaids, and centaurs were popular in Europe. Pearl's prestige continued into the nineteenth century. The gem collection of Dowager Empress Tz'hsi (1835-1908) included thousands of precious gems, many pearls among them, and she owned a cape embroidered with 3,500 pearls, each the size of a canary's egg.

In the early twentieth century, pearl prices remained prohibitive for many, but by the 1920s wealthy American women had ropes of pearls rivaling those of European royalty and Asian potentates. In the 1930s, two events changed pearl's future drastically—the Great Depression and the introduction of cultured pearls.

The spherical cultured pearl was first produced in Japan in about 1907. The creator of the industry is Kokichi Mikimoto (d. 1955), known as "The Pearl King." Fine jewelry stores rejected cultured pearls initially; Tiffany & Co. did not sell them until 1956. Today, although natural pearls may be up to ten times more expensive than equivalent cultured pearls, the natural ones amount to less than 10 percent of the total pearl trade in value.

Legends and Lore

PEARLS, IN INDIAN MYTHOLOGY, WERE HEAVENLY dewdrops that fell into the sea and were caught by shellfish under the first rays of the rising sun during a period of full moon, a belief adopted by Europeans. According to Hebrew legend, pearls are the tears shed by Eve when she was banished from Eden. For the ancient Chinese, pearls represented wealth, honor, and longevity. Pearls were widely used as medicine in Europe until the seventeenth century. The lowest-grade pearls are still ground and used as medicine in the Orient.

Occurrences

COMMERCIAL FISHING FOR NATURAL PEARLS IS essentially nonexistent, but in the past it was important in the Persian Gulf and the Gulf of Mannar between India and Sri Lanka. In addition to Japan, cultured salt-water pearls are produced in Australia and a few equatorial islands in the Pacific, where warmer waters and a larger mollusc permit the growth of larger pearls. The largest and finest pearls, famous for their creamy color and fine pink orient, are produced in Burma's pearl farms.

There are over 100 fresh-water pearl farms in Lake Biwa, Honshu, Japan. Biwa pearls are usually white with fine luster and baroque shape. Fresh-water cultured pearls are also produced in China, Australia, and, most recently, Tennessee.

Fresh-water United States pearls and a shell measuring 9.5 cm (3 3/4 in.) wide and containing a blister pearl and a long hinge pearl.

*West Indian emperor
helmet shell cameo,
"Chariot of the Muses," a
late nineteenth-century
Italian work.*

Evaluation

DISTINCTION BETWEEN NATURAL AND FINE CULTURED pearls can be accomplished conclusively only by X-radiography. Important factors for both are size, shape, color, and orient. The most valued shape is a perfect sphere, followed by symmetrical drop, pear, and button. A perfect pearl is a semitranslucent sphere with even color, fine orient, deep luster, and fine texture. Highly valued colors are white and cream with pink overtones and black with iridescent green orient. Most cultured pearls are bleached. Many are tinted pink and sometimes dyed to imitate naturally-colored black pearls. Occasionally, pearls are irradiated to produce gray, gray blue, and black colors. The colors are permanent.

Pearls in a necklace should be matched in color, luster, and translucency and strung with knots between them to prevent rubbing—also ensuring that only one pearl will be lost if the string breaks.

The thickness of the nacreous layers is important for cultured pearls. Pearls with a coating of less than one-fiftieth inch are considered low quality. Lacquer is often applied to prevent cracking and wear. Cheap imitation pearls are made of plastic or glass beads with a thin coating of synthetic pearl essence. Finer imitations consist of opalescent glass beads dipped many times into a solution of guanine (manufactured from fish scales), then polished and coated with lacquer to prevent discoloration. Majorcan imitation pearls are known for their good quality.

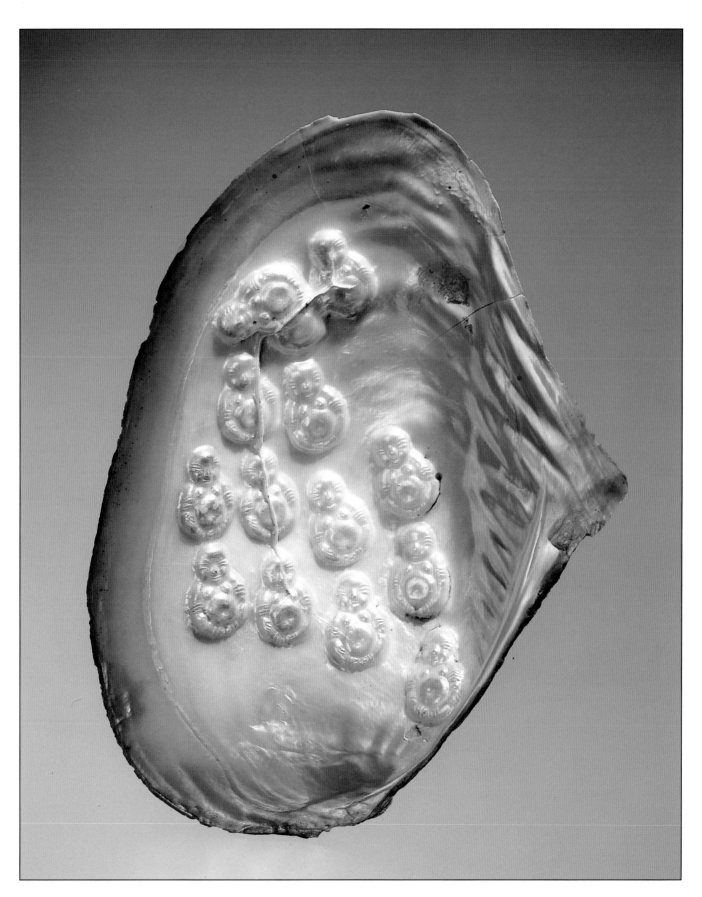

Small lead Buddah figures were implanted in a live fresh-water mussel and became covered with mother of pearl. The shell measures 11.3 cm (5 in.) across.

AMBER

Greek philosopher Thales (sixth century B.C.) noted that, after it has been rubbed, amber attracts lightweight objects. The Greeks termed the substance *elektron*, a word associated with the sun. Thus the Greek name for amber is the word from which words like *electron* and *electric* derive. *Amber* derives from the Arabic *ambar*, meaning "amber-gris," a substance obtained from the sperm whale and used in making perfumes.

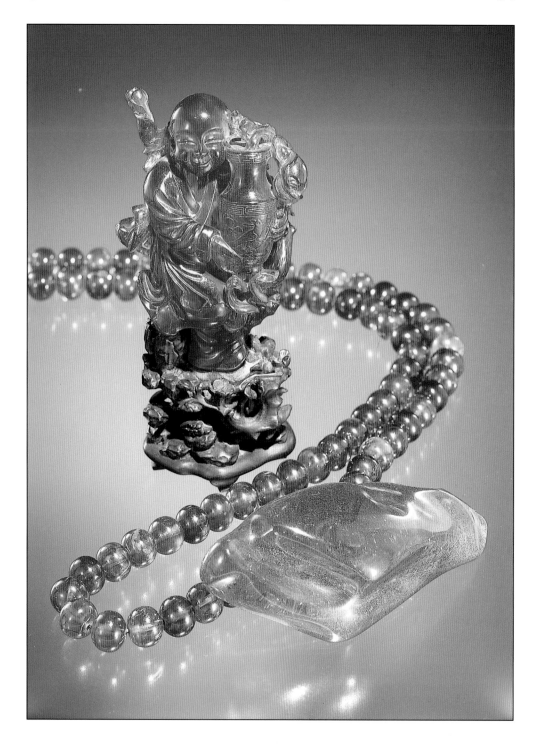

(Left) Chinese carving of amber 10.9 cm (4 1/4 in.) high, a string of 108 beads from the Baltic Coast, and irregular polished piece from Sicily, 11.5 cm (4 1/2 in.) long.

(Opposite) Amber dress ornament carved in China and of Burmese origin, 7 cm (2 3/4 in.) across.

Amber Data

Chemical formula:	*A mixture of hydrocarbons*
Cleavage:	*None, but sometimes brittle*
Hardness:	*2-2.5*
Specific gravity:	*1.05-1.096*
R.I.:	*1.54*
Luster:	*Resinous*
Colors:	*Yellow, brown, whitish or red; occasionally green and blue caused by fluorescence or interference of light by included air bubbles*

Properties

AMBER IS COMPOSED OF FOSSILIZED NATURAL BOTANIC resins of various sorts. Amber is transparent to translucent, often found in sizable pieces, and often contains interesting inclusions—flora and small arthropods trapped by the once-fluid resins. Such fossils date to as early as the Cretaceous Period, 120 million years ago. Amber is soft but relatively tough, capable of being drilled and carved. Its specific gravity is so low that it floats in a saturated salt solution—a quality that distinguishes it from substitutes, which sink.

Some reserve the term "true amber," sometimes called "succinite," for amber from the Baltic region. Baltic amber is derived from various coniferous trees that lived 30 to 60 million years ago. Dominican amber is somewhat younger than Baltic amber and probably derives from a leguminous plant. Dominican amber is also softer than Baltic amber.

Amber 1.3 cm (1/2 in.) wide from Kinkora, New Jersey, containing the oldest known bee from the Cretaceous Period, about 80 million years old.

Classification of Baltic Amber

Clear amber:	**Transparent**
Fatty amber:	**Full of small air bubbles, resembling goose fat**
Bastard amber:	**Clouded because of the presence of many bubbles**
Bone amber:	**White or brown, more opaque than bastard amber**
Foamy or frothy amber:	**Opaque, with a chalky appearance**

Historic Notes

AMBER PENDANTS, BEADS, AND BUTTONS DATING TO 3700 B.C. have been found in Estonia, and amber treasures found in Egypt date as early as 2600 B.C. Amber beads from 2000 B.C. have been found in Crete and Mycenae, and graduated beads are of a similar age in England. In 1000 B.C., the Phoenicians were trading Baltic amber in the Mediterranean region. In Etruria (west central Italy) amber was used in fashioning inlays, beads, scarabs, and small-figure pendants. Amber has been burned as incense since early Christian times.

During the Middle Ages in Europe, the demand for use as rosary beads consumed the available amber. As the supply increased, so did amber's popularity. The skill of amber carving reached a peak in the sixteenth and seventeenth centuries; examples of carved objects include chalices, candlesticks and chandeliers, religious sculpture, and jewelry. During the nineteenth century, amber jewelry was very popular; but attention focused on the intrinsic value of the gem rather than on workmanship. Today, most amber is simply polished to display the gem's natural beauty and warm glow.

Legends and Lore

IN GREEK MYTHOLOGY, AMBER WAS FORMED WHEN Phaeton, son of Helios, the sun god, was killed by lightning. Grief turned his sisters to poplar trees; their tears were drops of amber.

Occurrences

NINETY PERCENT OF THE WORLD'S GEM-QUALITY amber is found along the southeastern shores of the Baltic Sea. Floating "sea" amber from these deposits is dispersed around the Baltic's shores. Most Baltic "pit" amber is mined from blue glauconite sand, called "blue earth." The largest deposits in this area are in the Samland Peninsula near Kaliningrad in the Soviet Union and around Gdansk in Poland. The second most important source is the Dominican Republic. Other occurrences are in Sicily (simetite), Burma (burmite), and Romania (romanite).

Evaluation

THE BEST-QUALITY AMBER IS CLEAR, TRANSPARENT, and flawless. The most valuable colors are greens, blues, and reds. Of the common colors, yellow is the most highly prized. Pressed amber or amberoid is made by heating small pieces of amber and hydraulically compressing them into blocks. Amberoid is distinguished from true amber by its flow structure and the elongation of air bubbles. Imitation amber is made with plastics, modern natural resins, or glass.

Fossilized ammonite, marketed as ammolite or korite, from northern Alberta in Canada, an 18.3-cm (7 1/8 in.) wide piece and two cabochons of 9.67 cts. and 41.98 cts.

CORAL

The orange-to-red gem often seen as Italian "horn" good-luck charms was long thought to be a sea plant with flowers but no leaves or roots. In 1723, the French biologist G.A. Peyssonel identified coral as the exoskeleton of colonial polyps, small animals that create their dendritic forms from calcite dissolved in sea water. Although coral is a potentially renewable resource, reckless exploitation has placed the corals in jeopardy of extinction. Conservation efforts, initiated in the 1970s, aim at selective harvesting to preserve the gem corals.

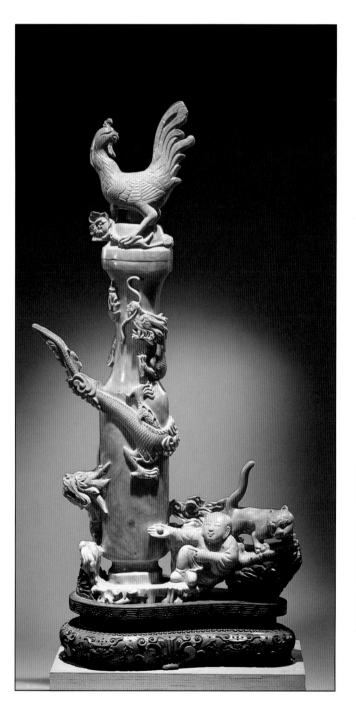

CORAL DATA

Coral is formed primarily of either calcite, CaCO$_3$, or conchiolin, a horny organic substance.

Cleavage:	*None*
Hardness:	*3.5-4*
Specific gravity:	*2.6-2.7 (red calcite coral); 1-3 (black, gold, blue conchiolin coral)*
R.I.:	*Not measurable*

Nineteenth-century Chinese coral carvings, 35.5 cm (14 in.) high.

Properties

RED COLOR IS THE DISTINCTIVE ATTRIBUTE OF THE traditional gem coral, although it ranges from red through orange to pink and even white. Red is due to iron and organic pigments, and fine skeletal structure renders coral opaque. The most valued gem coral is created by the coelenterate species *Corallium rubrum*, a hard coral. Black coral, known as "akbar" or "king's coral," golden coral, and the rare gray blue "akori" are soft corals. The lengthwise striped or patterned skeletal structure to their branches distinguishes all corals from imitations.

Historic Notes

CORAL HAS BEEN FOUND WITH PALEOLITHIC REMAINS in Wildscheuer Cave, north of Wiesbaden, Germany. It was depicted on a Sumerian vase of about 3000 B.C. Coral was popular with the ancient Greeks and Romans. Pliny, writing in the first century A.D., mentions coral trade between the Mediterranean countries and India. In the thirteenth century, Marco Polo noted coral in jewelry and adorning idols in Tibetan temples. Chinese mandarins wore coral buttons of office. The Spaniards introduced coral to Mesoamerica during the sixteenth century, and the Navajo and Pueblos used it extensively in jewelry.

The Victorians favored coral, and it was a favorite of Art Deco jewelers. Today, coral enjoys great popularity, but the supply will probably decrease or even cease if conservation efforts are unsuccessful.

Legends and Lore

CORAL IN GREEK MYTHOLOGY ORIGINATED WITH Medusa's death at the hands of Perseus; the drops of her blood became red coral. Coral amulets were thought to protect children from danger during Roman times. In "Metamorphosis," Roman poet Ovid (c. 43 B.C.-A.D. 17)

praised it as a cure for scorpion and serpent bites. Coral has promoted good humor, according to Arab physician Avicenna (A.D. 980-1037). A twelfth-century English manuscript recommends coral engraved with a gorgon or serpent as protection against all enemies and wounds. A medieval English belief was that a coral necklace helps in childbirth. In Italy to this day, coral is worn as protection against the "evil eye."

Occurrences

CORAL GROWS IN CLEAR, SHALLOW WARM WATER AT depths of about 10 to 45 feet. The sources of the finest coral from early times have been the Mediterranean and Red Seas, and the center of the coral industry, Torre del Greco, south of Naples, Italy, is also known as the City of Coral.

Two species of black coral were discovered in 1957 off Maui; this coral is also found off Australia and the West Indies. And a pink coral, previously known from other regions, was discovered in 1966 off Oahu. Gold coral is the rarest of the Hawaiian corals and varies in color from gold, brownish gold, bamboo beige, or brown to dark olive green. Coral is also found in the coastal waters of Japan, Malaysia, Australia, Ireland, and Mauritius.

Evaluation

COLOR, SIZE, AND POLISH DETERMINE CORAL'S VALUE. Pale rose ("angel skin") and deep red ("ox blood") are the most valued, and coral is sometimes stained to produce a more valuable shade. Large pieces are rare, and large, fine carvings command high prices. Necklaces are evaluated by matching color and evenness of the beads.

Coral is imitated with conch pearl, conch shell, and powdered marble compacted under pressure. Plastics, wood, and sealing wax are also used. The Gilson coral, produced in orange to red colors, is an excellent recent imitation.

JET

Though jet has an ancient tradition and was a charm of good fortune, not long ago it was associated with mourning jewelry. Queen Victoria wore it for forty years following Prince Albert's death in 1861, raising jet's popularity to its pinnacle. But by the early twentieth century, fashion changed, and the jet jewelry industry vanished. Today, with black in vogue, jet's popularity has revived.

Jet Data

Composition:	*Carbon plus various hydrocarbon compounds*
Cleavage:	*None, but brittle*
Hardness:	*3-4*
Specific gravity:	*1.3-1.35*
R.I.:	*About 1.66*

Properties

JET IS A DARK BROWN TO BLACK VARIETY OF LIGNITE (derived from the Latin *lignum,* meaning "wood"), a low-grade coal. Jet will burn. It takes a high polish but scratches and abrades easily. It is sufficiently tough to be carved and faceted; a softer, brittle and less "workable" variety is called "bastard jet." Rubbed vigorously on wool or silk, jet develops an electric charge and attracts small pieces of straw or paper. This similarity to amber earned it the name "black amber."

Historic Notes

JEWELRY FROM BRITAIN DATES FROM THE MIDDLE OF the second millennium B.C., and the area around Whitby on the northeast coast of England has been the major source of the finest jet in the world. During Roman times, jet mining in Britannia was active, and a significant amount of jet jewelry made in Eburacum (York) was shipped to Rome. According to Pliny, the material was named for the town and river Gagas in Lycia (Turkey), where it or a similar substance was found.

Jet carving flourished in Spain during the fourteenth and fifteenth centuries, when jet was used in talismans and during periods of mourning. Pre-Columbian Mayas, Aztecs, Pueblos, and Native Alaskans used jet as decoration. The eighteenth and nineteenth centuries saw jet's extensive use in rosaries, crosses, carvings, and jewelry.

A polished jet slab 9.5 cm (3 3/4 in.) long, a faceted jet stone of 2.92 cts., an oval cabochon of 5.26 cts. All from unknown localities. The jet and turquoise frog from Chaco Canyon in New Mexico, measuring 8.1 cm (3 3/16 in.) in height, from the Department of Anthropology at the Museum.

Legends and Lore

JET HAS BEEN CONSIDERED PROTECTIVE, A GEM FOR seafarers. It drives away venomous beasts, according to a book written in 1213 by Ibnu'I Baitar, an Arabian botanist. Since the tenth century, Spanish jet *hijas,* a hand-shaped talisman, has been worn as protection from the evil eye.

Occurrences

JET IS FOUND IN LENTICULAR MASSES EMBEDDED IN hard black bituminous shale, known as "jet rock," where it formed by the lithification of submerged driftwood in sea-floor mud. Jet is found in Germany, Spain, France, Poland, the United States, the Soviet Union, and India, as well as in England.

Evaluation

UNIFORM COLOR AND TEXTURE ARE THE MAJOR FACTORS to be considered. The compact homogeneous hard types take better polish and are considered the finest quality. Jet is moderately priced.

GEMSTONES CONFUSED WITH JET, JET SUBSTITUTES, AND IMITATIONS

Obsidian, dyed chalcedony, and black tourmaline can be confused with jet. Scotch cannel coal and Pennsylvania anthracite have been used as substitutes. Imitation jet is made with glass, plastics, and vulcanite (hard vulcanized rubber). Black glass stones are often known as "Paris jet."

Rare & Unusual Gemstones & Ornamental Material

Many minerals—for lack of sufficient abundance, uniformly good properties, or a popular tradition—do not rank among the better known gems. Some are beautiful but not suited for use in jewelry and are mainly of interest to collectors. In this chapter, gem minerals have been segregated from the carving materials; this separates the facetable crystals from the rocks or "ornamental material." These gem minerals, often called "the rare and unusual gemstones," have been sorted into three categories: (1) minerals that have excellent properties but are too rare or are not so rare but have only adequate properties—usually lacking sufficient color or brilliance; (2) gem crystals that are too soft or fragile to be anything other than collectors' stones or part of a museum exhibition; and (3) opaque metallic minerals that have been faceted and fashioned for use in jewelry. The ornamental materials are listed last.

Tanzanite crystal from Tanzania measuring 4.2 cm (1 5/8 in.) in height.

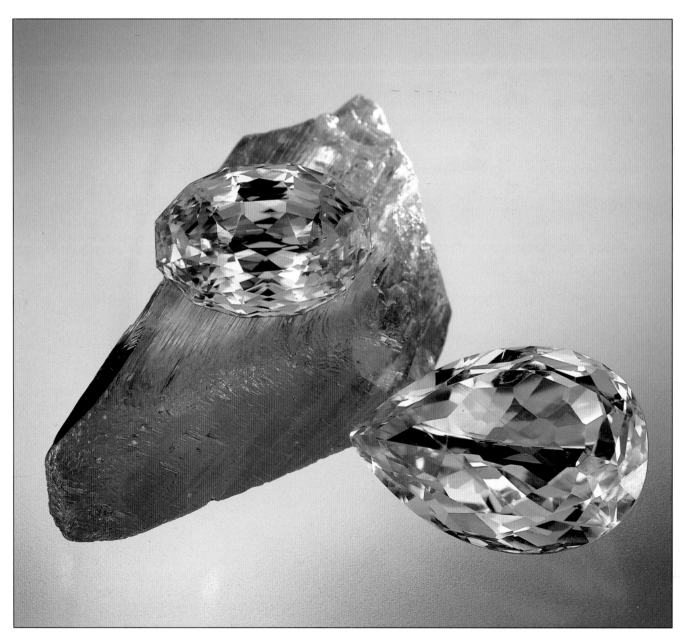

A kunzite crystal 9.8 cm (3 13/16 in.) long and two cut stones of 121.48 and 191.84 cts. from Pala, California.

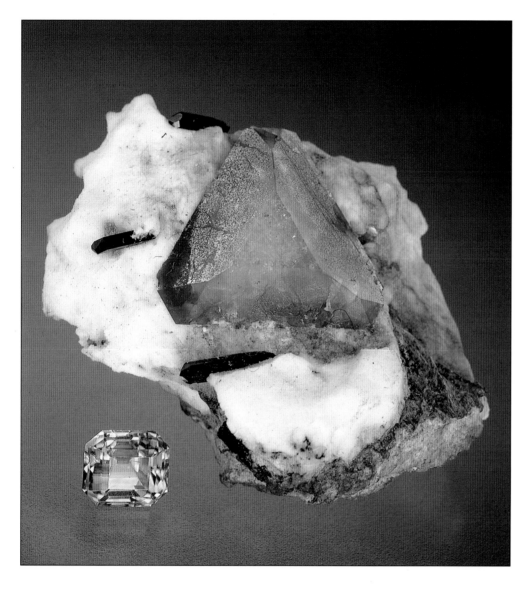

A 3.57-ct. benitoite gem and a crystal measuring 2 cm (3/4 in.) across, with neptunite crystals in natrolite matrix. Both are from San Benito County, California.

The entries in each group are ranked in descending order of "gem quality," a somewhat subjective evaluation. (See table, pages 200–201, for specific data on each mineral; some rare ones are also included only in this table.) We fully acknowledge our own biases in this ranking.

Very Rare and Moderately Good Gemstones

Zoisite was first described in 1905, and the pink variety, thulite, particularly from Norway, was used as an ornamental stone for cabochons and carvings. In 1967, a new, magnificent intense blue variety from Tanzania was named *tanzanite* by Henry B. Platt, vice-president of Tiffany & Co., the firm that created a market for this gem. The crystals are transparent, sapphire blue to amethyst violet, and very strongly pleochroic. Some tanzanite is heat-treated to eliminate yellow or brown tinges and deepen the blue color. Because of its magnificent color and beauty, tanzanite has become popular as a faceted gem.

Benitoite was discovered in San Benito County, California, in 1907 and recently established as that state's gem, since it is found nowhere else. This rare gem has the color of blue sapphire and the dispersion of diamond.

Spodumene varies in color from colorless to

yellow, yellow green, pink, violet, pale to deep green, and pale green blue. *Kunzite* and *hiddenite* are the two most popular gem varieties. Kunzite is pink, lilac, or violet and was named after the famous gemologist George F. Kunz. Some kunzites fade on prolonged exposure to sunlight. Major sources are California, Brazil, and Afghanistan. Hiddenite is a rare gem, restricted in occurrence almost exclusively to Hiddenite, North Carolina.

Kornerupine

can be colorless, brown, and yellow, but green is the most valued color. Cat's eye and star kornerupine are very rare. Gem-quality material was first found in the Malagasy Republic in 1911; eastern Africa is an important source.

Sinhalite

was identified in 1952 and named after Sinhala, the ancient Sanskrit name for Sri Lanka, where the gem was found. It also occurs in Burma and Tanzania (pink to brownish pink). Previously, sinhalite was considered as brown peridot. Its typical colors are yellowish brown, greenish, and very dark brown.

Rutile

is a common titanium-rich mineral. Its color is usually dark red or reddish brown to black. It is characterized by high refractive indexes and very strong dispersion. Its fire exceeds by six times that of diamond but is usually masked by dark colors. The rarity of transparent material and the darkness of the colors restricts its use to collectors.

Euclase

is usually transparent and varies from colorless to assorted colors; blue is the most prized. The name derives from the Greek *eu*, meaning "easy," and *klasis*, meaning "fracture," in allusion to the mineral's perfect cleavage. If the supply were not so limited, it could be a popular gem; Minas Gerais, Brazil, is a major source for gem-quality euclase.

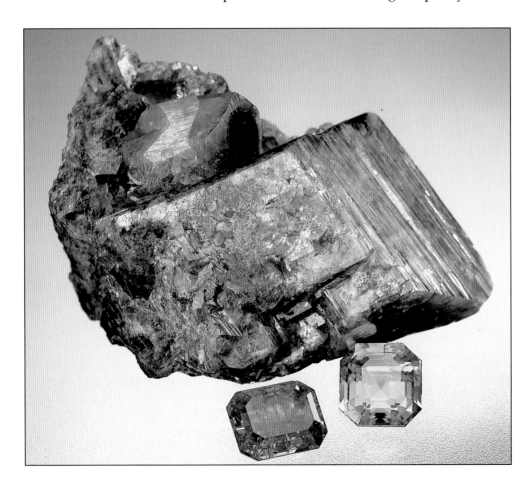

(Above) A kunzite crystal from Nuristan, Afghanistan, 14.5 cm (5 3/4 in.) high.

(Left) A group of color-zoned euclase crystals, the largest of which is 5.5 cm (2 1/8 in.) long, from Zimbabwe; and two cut gems of 7.94 cts. and 8.64 cts., from Minas Gerais, Brazil.

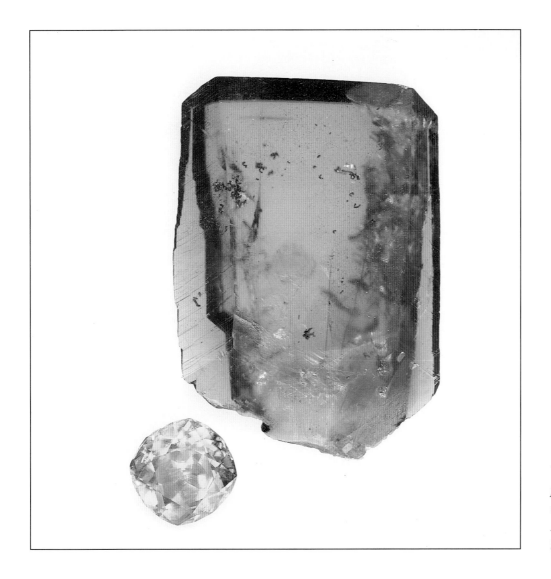

Titanite: a 10.07-ct. stone from Switzerland and a twinned crystal from Austria, 5.5 cm (2 1/8 in.) long.

Titanite, also known as *sphene*, is yellow, brown, or green and in gem quality is transparent. It has high refractive indexes and strong dispersion, giving the well-cut stones high brilliance and fire. It would be an important gem mineral if it were harder and less brittle. Gem titanite is found in the Malagasy Republic, Brazil, and Mexico.

Diopside is a member of the pyroxene group of rock-forming minerals, seldom found in gem quality. Occasionally, it is cut into faceted stones, cat's eyes, and four-rayed star stones. It most commonly occurs in different shades of green. India, China, and New York are important sources of gem diopside.

Obsidian is the most important of the natural glasses for use in jewelry. Obsidian is a transparent to opaque volcanic glass; it is usually black but may also be brown, green, yellow, red, or blue. Occasionally, it exhibits a golden or silver

iridescent sheen caused by reflection from tiny inclusions. *Snowflake,* or *flowering,* obsidian is a black variety with white inclusions. *Mahogany obsidian* is a banded black and red variety. *Apache tears* are small rounded pebble-like pieces, usually translucent and light to dark gray in color, found in the American West. Major occurrences are worldwide.

Scapolite is actually a mineral group and may be colorless, pink, violet, yellow, or gray. It makes attractive cat's eyes and faceted stones. Gem-quality scapolite was first found in 1913 in Mogok, Burma, but the Malagasy Republic and Brazil are also sources.

Amblygonite of gem quality is usually yellow, greenish yellow, or lilac. The relative rarity and pale colors of amblygonite restrict its use in jewelry. The major sources of gem amblygonite are Brazil, Burma, and Maine in the United States.

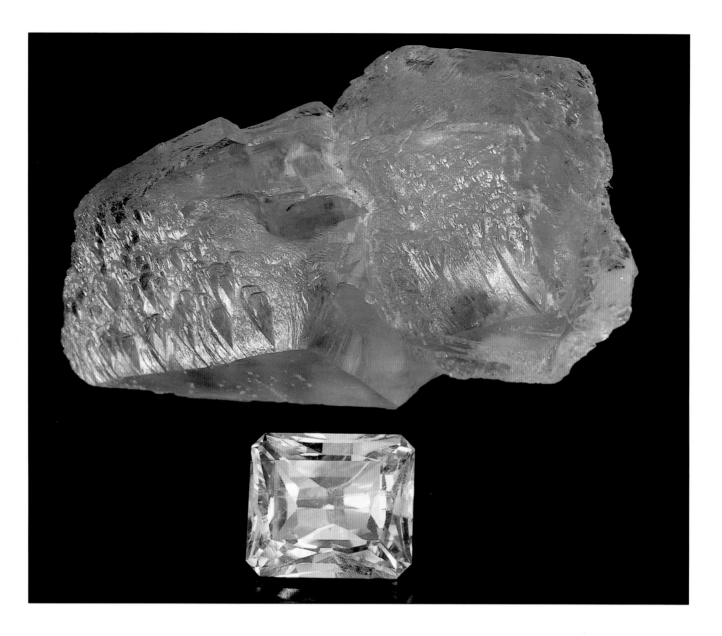

Soft and Fragile Gemstones

Calcite is the most common carbonate mineral and is very abundant. Aragonite is chemically identical to calcite but has a different crystal structure. Faceting calcite is difficult because it has perfect cleavage in three directions. Calcite may be colorless, white, gray, red, pink, green, yellow, brown, or blue. *Iceland spar* is the transparent colorless variety of calcite. Gem-quality calcite is found in many localities, particularly Mexico. *Marble* is a metamorphic rock consisting predominantly of calcite and used for statues and decorative objects. *Onyx marble* is banded calcite and/or aragonite. Its major source is Baja California in Mexico, and hence it is occasionally called "Mexican onyx" or, if dyed green, "Mexican jade."

Fluorite is fragile but occurs in a wide variety of colors. *Fluorescence* derives its name from this

mineral, which displays the property vividly. Because of its attractive colors, it is occasionally faceted for collectors. The variety banded in white and blue, violet, or purple—known as Blue John or Derbyshirespar—has been used since Roman times for ornamental objects. Southern Illinois is a major source of fluorite.

Rhodochrosite has been used commercially for decorative objects, beads, and cabochons since a beautifully banded massive material was discovered at San Luis in Argentina before World War II. Rhodochrosite from Argentina is occasionally referred to as "Inca Rose" because the Inca worked the same deposits. Rhodochrosite is also found as deep red crystals, which are occasionally faceted for collectors, particularly those from Hotazel, South Africa.

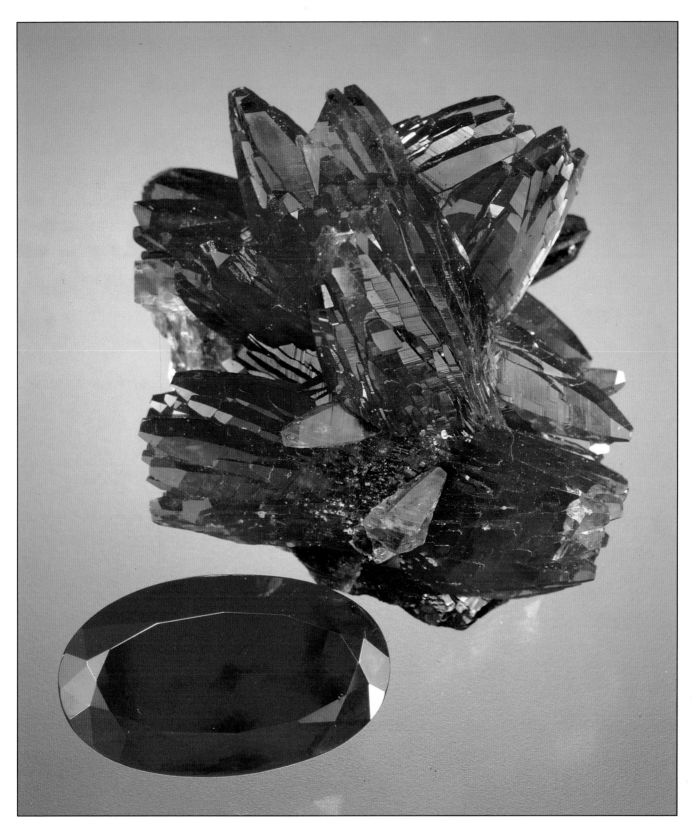

(Above) A 59.65-ct. rhodochrosite gem from Kuruman, South Africa, the largest on record, and a group of crystals that is 7.0 cm (2 3/4 in.) wide.

(Opposite) Amblygonite cut stone of 34.00 cts. and an irregular crystal of gem-quality amblygonite 8 cm (3 1/8 in.) high from Minas Gerais, Brazil.

Metallic Opaque Gemstones

Pyrite, known as "fool's gold," is the most common sulfide mineral and occurs throughout the world. When used in jewelry, it has been called "marcasite." This is a misnomer; marcasite, though chemically identical, is a mineral with a different crystal structure. Pyrite was used by the ancient Greeks and Romans, Mayas, Aztecs, and Incas. Its popularity revived in the late 1980s.

Pyrite is opaque with a brass-yellow color and bright metallic luster.

Hematite, one of the most important ores of iron, is black to dark gray with a metallic luster. It is fashioned into intaglios, cameos, and occasionally beads imitating black pearls or faceted stones often sold as black diamonds. There are many sources; Alaska is now a major one.

Calcite crystal 7.3 cm (2 7/8 in.) long and a 99.6-ct. gem from Gallatin County, Montana.

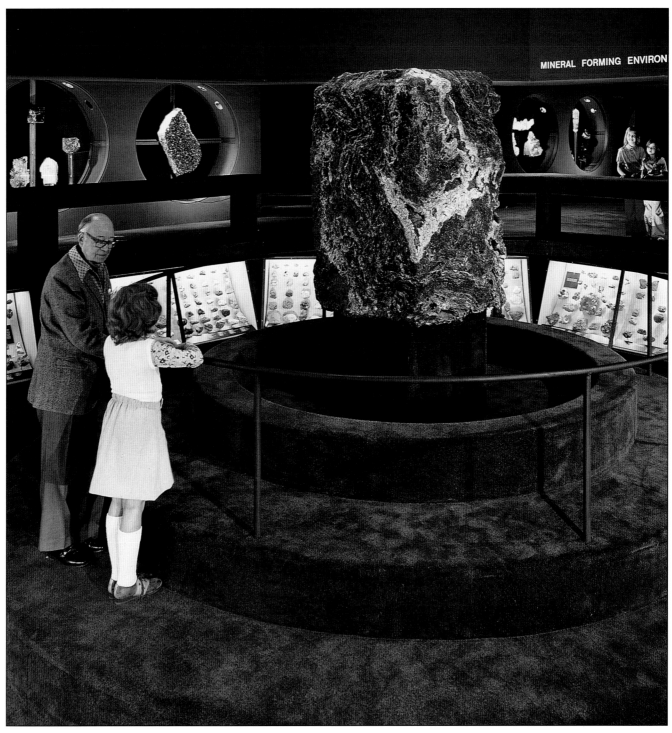

A 4 1/2-ton block of azurite-malachite 5 feet tall from the Copper Queen Mine in Bisbee, Arizona.

(Above) A polished slice of intergrown azurite and malachite from Bisbee, Arizona. It is 7.5 cm (3 in.) in diameter.

(Opposite) Chinese malachite vase, 20 cm (7 7/8 in.) high.

Ornamental Material—Carvings, Beads, Inlays

Gypsum has three varieties that have been used as ornamental stones since ancient times. *Alabaster* is the massive, fine-grained, translucent variety. *Satin spar* is the fibrous variety with a pearly luster. *Selenite* is the transparent colorless crystal form. Gypsum is very soft and can be scratched with a fingernail. It is usually white, but it may also be yellowish, brownish, reddish, or greenish. The massive variety is porous and is easily dyed. The most important sources of alabaster are Tuscany, Italy, and Derbyshire and Staffordshire, England.

Talc, when free from admixture, is silvery white but with impurities becomes gray, green, reddish, brown, or yellow. It is the softest gem mineral. *Steatite,* a popular material for carvings, is massive talc containing impurities that increase its hardness. It has a greasy, soapy feel and is also known as soapstone. The translucent material has a higher value than the opaque. *Agalmatolite* is a brownish variety of steatite. Steatite occurs at many locations.

Pyrophyllite is a rare mineral occasionally used for cabochons and more frequently for carvings. It is soft and usually opaque, has a pearly to greasy luster and comes in colors varying from white to gray, pale blue, and brown. Translucent material is the most valued. A considerable part of the so-called *agalmatolite,* commonly used

in Chinese carvings, is compact pyrophyllite. An important source is China.

Malachite is a vivid green copper mineral widely used for cabochons, beads, carvings, and inlaid work. It was known in Egypt as early as 3000 B.C. and was used for amulets, jewelry, and, as powder, for eye shadow. In the early nineteenth century, the famous Ural mines were highly productive and supplied malachite to Europe. It was worn in Italy as an amulet against the evil eye. Malachite seldom occurs in visible crystals but is usually massive or fibrous. The massive variety, banded in two green hues, is the most attractive for jewelry. Malachite is soft, brittle, and sensitive to heat, acids, and ammonia—not sufficiently durable for ring stones. Currently, the major producer of malachite is Zaire.

Azurite is an intense azure blue, soft and opaque gem. Most often cabochons, beads, or decorative objects are fashioned from massive azurite. Important sources are Tsumeb, Namibia and China.

Rhodonite in its massive form is popular for cabochons, beads, vases, boxes, goblets, and other decorative objects. It was first used in Russia in the late eighteenth century. Rhodonite has an attractive rose red color, usually with black veins of manganese oxides. Major sources are in the Ural Mountains of the Soviet Union and Japan.

RARE AND UNUSUAL GEMS

SPECIES VARIETY	CHEMICAL FORMULA	HARDNESS	SPECIFIC GRAVITY	REFRACTIVE INDEX	COMMENT
VERY RARE GEMSTONES					
Zoisite	$Ca_2Al_3(SiO_4)_3(OH)$	6–6.5	3.15–3.38	1.685–1.725	
Tanzanite—a beautiful blue pleochroic variety rare					
Thulite—a massive pink ornamental stone					
Benitoite	$BaTiSi_3O_9$	6–6.5	3.64–3.7	1.757–1.804	sapphire-blue, strong fire, very rare
Spodumene	$LiAlSi_2O_6$	6.5–7	3.0–3.20	1.660–1.676	good cleavage in two directions
Kunzite—lilac colored, some popularity					
Hiddenite—emerald green, exceedingly rare					
Kornerupine	$Mg_3Al_6(Si,Al,B)_5O_{21}(OH)$	6–7	3.28–3.35	1.661–1.699	green to brown and rare
Rutile	TiO_2	6–6.5	4.2–4.3	2.62–2.90	dark and somewhat soft
Sinhalite	$MgAlBO_4$	6.5–7	3.47–3.5	1.665–1.712	mistaken for brown peridot
Euclase	$BeAlSiO_4(OH)$	6.5–7.5	3.05–3.1	1.650–1.676	one perfect cleavage; rare
Titanite	$CaTiSiO_5$	5–5.5	3.44–3.55	1.843–2.11	fine brilliance and fire but soft
Diopside	$CaMgSi_2O_6$	5–6	3.2–3.3	1.664–1.721	green pyroxene, rare in multi-carat sizes
Obsidian	natural glass	5–5.5	2.40	1.48–1.51	usually dark, brittle
Scapolite	$(Ca,Na)_4Al_3(Al,Si)_3$-$Si_6O_{24}(Cl,CO_3,SO_4)$	5–6	2.50–2.74	1.539–1.579	in various colors and cat's eyes
Amblygonite	$(Li,Na)AlPO_4(F,OH)$	5.5–6	3.0–3.1	1.578–1.619	various pale colors and rare
SOME COLLECTOR GEMSTONES					
Calcite	$CaCO_3$	3	2.70	1.486–1.658	high birefringence, soft; perfect cleavage in 3 directions
Iceland Spar—optically flawless colorless calcite					
Fluorite	CaF_2	4	3.18	1.434	many colors, soft, octahedral cleavage
Rhodochrosite	$MnCO_3$	3.5–4.5	3.45–3.6	1.97–1.817	soft with 3 cleavages—massive form ornamental stone
Barite	$BaSO_4$	3–3.5	4.3–4.6	1.636–1.648	various colors but soft and 1 perfect cleavage

RARE AND UNUSUAL GEMS

SPECIES VARIETY	CHEMICAL FORMULA	HARDNESS	SPECIFIC GRAVITY	REFRACTIVE INDEX	COMMENT
METALLIC GEMSTONES					
Pyrite	FeS_2	6–6.5	5.02		brassy, called macasite in marketplace
Hematite	Fe_2O_3	5.5–6.5	5.26		steely black, called black diamonds
ORNAMENTAL MATERIALS					
Gypsum Alabaster—massive fine grained rock Satin spar—fibrous with pearly luster Selenite—transparent colorless crystal	$CaSO_4 \cdot 2(H_2O)$	2	2.3	1.520–1.530	soft and abundant
Talc Steatite or Soapstone—massive fine grained rock, often apple green	$Mg_3Si_4O_{10}(OH)_2$	1	2.2–2.8	1.54	soft and greasy feeling
Pyrophyllite Agalmatolite—creamy white to brown massive form	$Al_2Si_4O_{10}(OH)_2$	1–2	2.65–2.90	1.58	soft, resembles talc
Malachite	$Cu_2CO_3(OH)_2$	3.5–4.5	3.6–4.1	1.85	light to dark green, banded and massive
Azurite	$Cu_3(CO_3)_2(OH)_2$	3.5–4	3.77	1.730–1.836	dark azure blue, alters to malachite
Rhodonite	$MnSiO_3$	5.5–6.5	3.57–3.76	1.73	rose, pink to brownish red, usually massive
Variscite	$AlPO_4 \cdot 2H_2O$	3.5–4.5	2.2–2.57	1.56	massive blue-green mistaken for turquoise
Serpentine Bowenite—green jadelike rock (Hardness = 4–6)	$Mg_3Si_2O_5(OH)_4$	2.5	2.44–2.62	1.56	commonly in soft green rock serpentinite

Glossary

Allochromatic Pertaining to color resultant from a mineral impurity, such as minor chemical substitutions or radiation damage.

Alluvial deposit See Placer deposit

Amulet See Talisman

Asterism Chatoyancy in two or more directions giving a starlike appearance in illumination.

Axis (or crystal axis) A reference direction in a crystal that is parallel to symmetry directions or the intersection of faces.

Birefringence is the magnitude of the difference in the R.I.s of birefringent minerals.

Birefringent (or doubly refractive) Having two or three refractive indices (R.I.s) a characteristic of minerals not possessing cubic symmetry.

Brilliance Degree to which faceted gem sparkles and returns light from within; dependent upon cut and refractive index. Synonyms: life, liveliness.

Cabochon A gem cut style distinguished by its smooth convex top and no facets.

Carat The standard unit of gem weight (mass); 1 ct. = 0.2 grams.

Chatoyancy Cat's eye appearance when stone is illuminated. Caused by parallel arrangement of tiny needles within a crystal

Cleavage The tendency of a mineral to break along a plane due to a direction of weakness in the crystal.

Cryptocrystalline Constituted of submicroscopic crystals.

Crystal A solid body having a regularly repeating arrangement of its atomic constituents; the external expression may be bounded by natural planar surfaces called "faces."

Crystalline Having the properties of a crystal: a regular internal arrangement in three dimensions of constituent atoms.

Cubic (crystal system) Defined by three mutually perpendicular axes of equal length—the highest symmetry class.

Dichroism Pleochroism in two directions.

Dispersion The systematic variation of refractive index with color in a substance; colors separate during refraction of white light. It leads to fire in a gem.

Fire Division of colors in a colorless transparent gem such as diamond; due to dispersion.

Gem A mineral (gemstone) that has been fashioned to enhance its natural beauty.

Gemstone A substance that has beauty, durability and rarity and that can be fashioned into personal adornment.

Group (mineral group) A set of minerals that share the same crystal structure.

Habit A characteristic shape of a mineral, either a crystal shape or the shape and style of polycrystalline intergrowths.

Hardness Resistance to scratching; measured from 1 to 10 on the Mohs scale.

Hexagonal (crystal system) Defined by three equal axes lying in a plane and intersecting at 120° angles and a fourth perpendicular axis that is a six-fold rotation.

Idiochromatic Color is inherent and due to some aspect of chemical composition and crystal structure.

Imitation A substance that simulates a genuine gem, although typically applied to glass, plastic and other non-crystalline materials.

Intergrowth A composite of crystals in intimate contact.

Iridescence Color produced by light interference, as in labradorite feldspar.

Luster The manner in which a substance reflects light from its surface; it is affected by the surface's smoothness and the substance's reflectivity.

Magma Mobile molten rock material from which igneous rocks form by solidification.

Mineral A naturally-occurring substance (usually inorganic) that is crystalline and has a composition that can be defined by a simple chemical formula.

Monoclinic (crystal system) Defined by three nonparallel axes where there are only two right angles between the axes and no high-order rotation axes.

Orthorhombic (crystal system) Defined by three unequal mutually perpendicular axes.

Pegmatite (gem) An igneous rock with conspicuously large mineral grains and often enriched with volatile elements in minerals such as beryl (Be), spodumene (Li), topaz (F) and tourmaline (B).

Piezoelectric Capable of producing a surface electric charge when deformed elastically; a property of some minerals without a center of symmetry.

Placer deposit An accumulation of dense mineral grains at the bottom of a sediment pile by the weathering action of a moving fluid such as water (alluvial deposit) or wind.

Play of colors A range of colors seen in a gemstone such as opal when it is viewed from different angles. The phenomenon is due to optical diffraction.

Pleochroism The phenomenon whereby the color intensity or the actual color is different depending on the orientation in which a crystalline substance is observed.

Pseudochromatic Coloring due to physical causes such as dispersion or foreign included particles and internal boundaries

Pyroelectric Capable of producing a surface electric charge when temperature changes; a property of some minerals that do not have a center of symmetry.

Refraction The bending of light (or any wave phenomenon) when it moves between media with different conductive velocities

Refractive index (R.I.) A mathematical constant equal to the ratio of the velocity of light in a vacuum to that in the substance; it determines the angle at which light bends when it enters a substance obliquely.

Rock A consolidated assemblage of grains of one or more minerals.

Rough The raw gemstone.

Schist A metamorphic rock having a subparallel alignment of the principal constituent mica or micalike (platy) minerals.

Simulant A substance used to simulate a gemstone, usually a synthetic material with a similar appearance to the simulated gemstone.

Sixling A twin intergrowth of six crystals that appears to have hexagonal symmetry; a common habit for chrysoberyl.

Specific gravity A dimensionless measure of density (numerically equivalent to the value in grams per cubic centimeter).

Symmetry The correspondence in shape or length of elements of a body; as repeated by a mirror, rotation about an axis, or inversion through a point (center of symmetry).

Synthetic A man-made substance that is identical to a natural one.

Talisman An object, sometimes fashioned and engraved with a symbol, that is believed to provide magical, medicinal, or protective power. Synonym: Amulet.

Tetragonal (crystal system) Defined by three mutually perpendicular axes, two of which are of equal length.

Trigonal (crystal system) Defined by three equal axes lying in a plane and intersecting at 120° angles and a fourth perpendicular axis that is a three-fold rotation axis.

Trilling A twin intergrowth of three crystals that appears to have trigonal symmetry.

Twin (twinned crystal) A nonparallel intergrowth of separate crystals related by symmetry not possessed by the substance.

Variety (gemstone) A named specific color or other quality of a gemstone species, such as ruby for red corundum.

Volatiles (components) In a magma, those materials that readily form a gas and are the last to enter into and crystallize as minerals during solidification.

ReadingList

Arem, Joel E. *Color Encyclopedia of Gemstones*, Second edition. New York, NY: Van Nostrand Reinhold, 1987. Best compendium of gem data; many good photos.

Ball, Sydney H. "Historical Notes on Gem Mining." *Economic Geology* 26 (1931): 681-738. An early and important effort on the history of mining.

Ball, Sydney H. *Roman Book on Precious Stones* (including an English modernization of the 37th *Book of Historie of the World* by Plinius Secondus). Santa Monica, California: Gemological Institute of America, 1950.

Bancroft, Peter. *Gem and Crystal Treasures.* Tucson, AR: Western Enterprises/ Mineralogical Record, 1984. A good compilation of information on mineral and gem localities.

Bauer, Max. *Precious Stones.* New York, NY: Charles E. Tuttle Company, 1982. One of the references on gems found in a good library.

Bruton, Eric. *Diamonds*, Second edition. Radnor, PA: Chilton, 1978. Excellent, authoritative, readable coverage of every aspect of diamonds.

Desautels, Paul. *Treasures in the Smithsonian: The Gem Collection.* Washington, DC: Smithsonian Institution Press, 1979. Very useful coverage of the Smithsonian Collection.

Desautels, Paul. *The Jade Kingdom.* New York, NY: Van Nostrand Reinhold, 1986. The best comprehensive book on jade.

Dietrich, R.V. *The Tourmaline Group.* New York, NY: Van Nostrand Reinhold, 1985. The authoritative book on tourmalines.

Evans, Joan. *Magical Jewels of the Middle Ages and the Renaissance.* Oxford, England: Clarendon Press, 1922. (New York, NY: Dover Publications, 1977) A scholarly work that cites directly from original texts on gems from ancient times through the seventeenth century.

Evans, Joan. A *History of Jewellery: 1100-1870.* Boston, MA: Boston Book and Art, 1970. An important and authoritative work.

Fraquet, Helen. *Amber.* London, UK: Butterworths, 1987.

Hunger, Rosa. *The Magic of Amber.* London, UK: N.A.G. Press, Ltd., 1977.

Hurlbut, Cornelius S., Jr., and Klein, C. *Manual of Mineralogy*, 20th edition. New York, NY: Wiley, 1977. A standard textbook on mineralogy.

Keller, Peter C. *Gemstones and Their Origins.* New York, NY: Van Nostrand Reinhold, 1990. A new book on the geological conditions of gemstone formation.

Kunz, George F., and Stevenson, Charles H. *The Book of the Pearl.* New York, NY: Century, 1908. Still an important book on pearl.

Kunz, George F. *The Curious Lore of Precious Stones.* New York, NY: Halcyon House, 1938 (1913). (Dover Publications, 1971.) A treasure trove of historical data and malarkey.

Kunz, George F. *The Magic of Jewels and Charms.* Philadelphia, PA: Lippincott, 1915. More wonderful information from the great gem expert.

Leechman, Frank. *The Opal Book.* Syndey, Australia: Ure Smith, 1978.

LeGrand, Jacques. *Diamonds: Myth, Magic, and Reality.* New York, NY: Crown, 1980. Coffee-table book on diamonds.

Liddicoat, Richard T., Jr. *Handbook of Gem Identification.* Santa Monica, CA: Gemological Institute of America. The American source on gem identification.

Meen, V.B., and Tushingham, A.D. *Crown Jewels of Iran.* Toronto, Ontario: University of Toronto Press, 1968. The incredible Iranian collection. Excellent photos.

Muller, Helen. *Jet.* London, UK: Butterworths, 1987. A treasure of information on jet.

Nassau, Kurt. *Gems Made by Man.* Radnor, PA: Chilton, 1980. Best book by far on gemstone synthetics and substitutes. Includes good section on color.

Nassau, Kurt. *Gemstone Enhancement*. London, UK: Butterworths, 1984. The authority on treatment, but already dated.

O'Donoghue, Michael. *Quartz*. London, UK: Butterworths, 1987. One of several books by a respected British gemologist.

Ogden, Jack. *Jewelry of the Ancient World*. New York, NY: Rizzoli, 1982. An important and definitive book.

Rouse, John D. *Garnets*. London, U.K.: Butterworths, 1986. One of a number of good books by Butterworths on individual gemstones.

Sinkankas, John. *Gemstones of North America*. New York, NY: Van Nostrand Reinhold, 1959. Vol. 2, 1976. Excellent book.

Sinkankas, John. *Emerald and Other Beryls*. Radnor, PA: Chilton, 1981. *The* book on the subject.

Smith, G.F. Herbert. *Gemstones*. London, UK: Chapman and Hall, 1972. An informative book on gems and their histories; few illustrations.

Tabriaux, Jean. *Pearls—their origin, treatment and identification*. London, UK: N.A.G. Press, 1985. An important new book on pearls.

Tait, Hugh. *Jewelry: 7,000 Years*. New York, NY: Harry N. Abrams, 1986. One of the imporant texts on history.

Webster, Robert. *Gems: Their Sources, Description, and Identification*. Archon Books, 1975. The most comprehensive book on gems.

Webster, Robert. *Gemologists' Compendium*. Sixth revised edition. London, UK: N.A.G. Press, Ltd., 1979. A gemologist's handbook.

Whitlock, Herbert P. *The Story of the Gems*. New York, NY: Garden City Publishing, 1940. The Museum's gem collection and gems in general. Dated.

Woodward, Christine, and Harding, Roger. *Gemstones*. New York, NY: Sterling Publishing, 1988. Good introductory book on gems; good pictures; British flavor.

Journals

Gems and Gemology. The quarterly of the Gemological Institute of America, Santa Monica, CA. The American journal on gemology.

Lapidary Journal. The amateur's journal, full of news, locality information, etc. Chilton Publishing, Radnor, PA.

Mineralogical Record. An amateur/professional journal on mineralogy. Fine articles on localities, species, and reviews for mineral collectors. Mineralogical Record Publishing, Tucson, AZ.

Index